THE LESSER ANTILLES

WITHDRAWN

ANDS

ANGUILLA
ST. MARTIN
ST. BARTHELEMY
SABA   BARBUDA
ST. EUSTATIUS
ST. KITTS
NEVIS   ANTIGUA
MONTSERRAT

EWARD
ANDS

GUADELOUPE

DOMINICA

WINDWARD

MARTINIQUE

ST. LUCIA

N
W   E
S

ISLANDS

ST. VINCENT   BARBADOS

GRENADA

TOBAGO

TRINIDAD

CONSERVATION
AND CARIBBEAN REGIONAL PROGRESS

A Crescent White Sand Beach of the South Shore
of Tobago

Conservation
and
Caribbean
Regional Progress

CARL A. CARLOZZI
ALICE A. CARLOZZI

illustrations by Christine Sena

published under the auspices of
THE CARIBBEAN RESEARCH INSTITUTE
of the College of the Virgin Islands,
St. Thomas, U.S. Virgin Islands

THE ANTIOCH PRESS

Preface

Over the past century, men and nations throughout the world have increasingly taken action to guarantee that the unique and beautiful places on the earth will be preserved as national parks. The implied social values and the technical methods vary from nation to nation, but there appears to be a universal human motivation underlying this national parks movement.

The Eastern Caribbean islands are rich in unique and beautiful places deserving of protection and care, but in the islands there is too little money and an absence of technical support for creating parks, reserves, and historic monuments. We conclude that money and technical help will have to come from outside the region. We write this book with the hope that more people will become concerned and will wish to take part in the efforts of the people of the Eastern Caribbean to preserve their national assets.

Very many people have, in many ways, helped us in doing our study. Throughout the islands their assistance was indispensable to our understanding of the conservation needs. We hope they will accept this book as our thanks to them.

The American Conservation Association, Incorporated, under the leadership of Mr. Laurance S. Rockefeller, President, has been the primary source of support for our work.

We are grateful to them for financial aid and for their steadfast belief in the cause of conservation in the Caribbean.

To our colleagues and friends at the Caribbean Research Institute, College of the Virgin Islands, we give our appreciation for their encouragement, enthusiasm, and for managing so well the more tedious chores of getting our book published.

C. A. C.
A. A. C.

Amherst, Massachusetts
June, 1967

Contents

List of Tables

PART ONE

Characteristics of the Islands

The Ruins of the Officers' Quarters at Brimstone
Hill Fort, St. Kitts

I
Introduction

Conceived in a cataclysmic dislocation of the earth's crust in the Cenozoic, born beneath the warm tropical sea, emerging with volcanic rumblings, fire, ash, and lava, mantled in places with ancient coral, etched and notched by the waves of unremembered seas, abraded by unknown hurricanes, incessantly watered by the moist, constant easterlies or nearly parched, cloaked in velvet green forest and thorny scrub—thus did the Caribbean islands await discovery by human kind. Men have lived gently on this land, and they have torn great wealth from it and from each other. Nature and human history have endowed the region with a rich diversity of remembrances pertinent to culture, history, science, and economics. This heritage of natural and historic resources is similar in present condition to like resources in most other parts of the world—scarce, dwindling, and largely unheeded by its inheritors. Yet in the Caribbean as elsewhere there is an awakening concern on the part of some people that these resources must be saved for the sake of memory and the advancement of knowledge.

The practical goals of this book are two-fold: first, to present at least a partial inventory of the natural and historic resources which are either unique or significant to the history and development of the islands; second, to discuss the present efforts and means for institutionalizing such resources in an active and continuing program of conservation.

We see the job as one of creating effective institutions for developing parks, reserves, historic monuments, and recreation areas both on a national basis and within an international, regional context. Success on the national level depends upon the capacity of the individual islands and countries of the region to create and support agencies able to acquire, preserve, and develop the appropriate resources. Successful international efforts will depend on the capacity of the islands and countries to establish an international institution serving as a regional forum and spokesman for the idea of conservation, through which persons outside the Caribbean can direct their moral support and tangible contributions to the region's conservation programs.

The general background conditions of the Eastern Caribbean, the magnitude of the relevant resources, and the possibilities for conservation action are taken up in turn in the three parts of this study.

Part One describes the biophysical nature of the islands, the impact which man has made upon them, and the present dynamics of social and economic organization.

Part Two presents an island-by-island inventory of places which have potential for development as national parks, nature reserves, historical sites, or public outdoor recreation areas.

Part Three discusses the need for physical planning on the islands and summarizes the basic problems that impede the conservation of natural and historic resources. It also suggests the kinds of assistance needed by the islands, encourages support for the Caribbean Conservation Association, and recommends the development of a Caribbean international park system.

II
Origins and History

Geology and climate

The land this book is about rises out of the eastern and southern edges of the Caribbean Sea in scattered bits and pieces. The total land area of the twenty-two islands dealt with is 4,915 square miles, slightly less than the area of the state of Connecticut. The largest island is Trinidad with an area of 1,860 square miles, and the smallest is Saba, 5 square miles.[1]

Sixteen of the islands are part of the double strand of islands that extends from east of Puerto Rico southward to the coast of South America. The inner or western arc of this chain began to form from submarine volcanoes during the late Oligocene. They emerged from the sea as active volcanic peaks, beginning in the Miocene with Martinique, Dominica, and western Guadeloupe and ending in the late Pliocene with St. Vincent. The outer or eastern arc, including Anguilla, Barbuda, Antigua, and eastern Guadeloupe, emerged from reefs formed on a submarine shelf or from reef-capped lateral lava flows. The volcanic islands all have one or more dominant peaks that are volcanic cones, eight of them still active. None of the sixteen islands is believed to have been contiguous with any continental land mass.

Aruba, Curacao, Bonaire, Trinidad, and Tobago were separated from the northern coast of South America during a subsidence of coastal land there in the late Oligocene. Barbados is at the eastern terminus of the Andean geological formation, but was never connected by land to South America.[2]

All of these islands lie between the Tropic of Cancer and the Equator and are in the broad bio-climatic zone of the Neotropics. They share in common aspects of climate such as wind direction, wind velocity, and average temperatures. Topographical features of the islands, their size and elevation, account for the great variations in rainfall; the mountainous islands receive more rainfall than islands with lower elevations. For example, the average annual precipitation of Aruba, Bonaire, and Curacao is only 22 inches, while in the Windward Islands it is about 88 inches.

On the mountainous islands, where peaks may be three to four thousand feet above sea level, average annual precipitation expressed as a single figure for an island gives little indication of the amount of rainfall at any given point on the island. On Dominica, for example, Mount Diablotin receives approximately 300 inches of rain each year, while the capital city of Rosseau on the southwest coast receives only 70 inches. While the extremes are not as great on other volcanic islands, the same pattern of variation exists.

The non-volcanic islands of the outer arc are relatively flat, with not many points reaching 1,000 feet. Rainfall is correspondingly less and is more evenly distributed than on the volcanic islands. The driest of the islands of the outer arc is Barbuda, with an average annual precipitation of about 35 inches.

The Amerindians[3]

The aboriginals of the Lesser Antilles are as yet unnamed by archeologists or anthropologists. Midden remains, the refuse heaps of prehistoric times, indicate that they were an early Stone Age culture exhibiting the simplest type of economy. When this primitive culture settled in the islands and how long they remained before being superceded by later Amerindian groups is unknown. Like their successors the Arawaks and the Caribs, the aboriginals are believed to have migrated from the South American mainland. Their record in the islands is a scanty one, and they left little to suggest mastery of any of the later Stone Age techniques in pottery, ornamentation, or tools.

By the time Columbus arrived in the West Indies, the only remaining pre-ceramic groups, the Ciboneys, were living in the western tips of Haiti and Cuba. However long the aboriginal culture may have been established in the West Indies and whatever its fate may have been, all archeological evidence points to the probability that it made very little physical impact upon the islands. Midden remains attributed to this group exhibit a predominance of shells and fish bones, indicating its gathering economy was based largely on food from the sea.

The Arawaks, the second Amerindian culture to migrate northward from the South American mainland, established the most advanced societies on the islands. The Arawaks' Neolithic culture was based upon a mixed economy of gathering and agriculture. Their settlements were found both along the coast and inland in fertile valleys where they cultivated soft forms of maize and cassava. Several subcultures of the Arawak civilization have been identified, all skilled in making ceramic vessels. It is by the various techniques of ceramic manufacture that the subcultures are identified.

No evidence has been found in the Lesser Antilles of Arawak dwellings made of durable materials. The Lesser Antilles were primarily a travel route to the Greater Antilles, where the Arawaks developed more permanent settlements. By the late fifteenth century, Arawaks were found in Puerto Rico, Hispañola, and Cuba, but not in the islands of the

Lesser Antilles to the east and south. There they had been supplanted by Caribs, the last Amerindian group to migrate from the Orinoco delta region up the Antillean arc.

The Caribs also had a Neolithic civilization. By archeological records, they were a somewhat more primitive people than the Arawaks, and more aggressive. Ceremonial cannibalism of enemy males is attributed to the Carib peoples. Their religious practices included the worship of Zemis, small idols carved with highly symbolic representations of animals and men. The Caribs left many petrographs and petroglyphs depicting the Zemi symbols carved or painted on large boulders or on the walls of caves and ancient wave notches eroded from sea cliffs.

Archeologists who have excavated Carib middens tend to agree that the Caribs probably acquired their knowledge of ceramic techniques as a result of their attacks on the Arawaks. Apparently, their usual procedure following a successful raid on an Arawak village was to kill all the males and enslave the females. Since the females were responsible for all household activities, the manual arts and the manufacture of pottery were continued by the Arawak women in the Carib villages and thus passed on to the Caribs.[4]

The warlike nature of the Caribs who occupied the larger islands of the Lesser Antillean group was a factor that delayed the eventual settlement and colonization of these islands by the European nations.

It is unfortunate for people interested in the study of the Amerindian cultures of the West Indies that these cultures left such an imperfect record of their life on the islands—little more than kitchen middens, petrographs, and petroglyphs. Because the archeological record of the islands' early inhabitants is so limited, there is an urgent need to preserve what little there is. Three and one-half centuries of settlement and exploitation have taken their toll of important archeological sites, and the loss of such sites has not stopped. Excavation of middens by casual and inept amateurs is a common occurrence, and vandalism at the sites of petroglyphs and petrographs can be observed anywhere these drawings and carvings are found.

Post-Columbian history[5]

The first voyage of Christopher Columbus to the New World culminated in the discovery and reconnaissance of the island of San Salvador in the Bahamas and the northern coasts of Hispañola and Cuba. In September, 1493, Columbus set sail from Cadiz, Spain, for his second journey, with seventeen ships loaded with people, material, and livestock to be settled in the new lands.

The more southerly course of the second voyage resulted in landfall at Dominica. The ships then sailed north and west along the arc of the outer islands to the Greater Antilles. A colony was established on the northern coast of Hispañola but removed a few years later to a more favorable location, the site of Santo Domingo.

During the early years of the sixteenth century, Spanish settlement was begun on Cuba and, to a lesser extent, Jamaica and Puerto Rico. The colonists raised cattle, tobacco, and sugar cane and mined gold in modest quantities. Hispañola and Cuba served as bases for expeditions sent out to explore the mainland and begin settling it.

The institution of slavery, later to play a major role in the economy and history of the Caribbean, was of minor importance during the early period of Spanish settlement. A few African slaves were brought with the earliest settlers. Several hundred additional slaves were brought from Africa to work in the gold mines of Hispañola. At first, slaves for the tobacco and sugar plantations were recruited from the Arawak Indians of the islands, but the Indians soon began to die out. Their unfenced fields of cassava and corn were trampled and grazed by herds of the Spaniards' pigs and cattle. Some Indians fought the Spaniards and were killed. Forced labor drove many to despair and suicide. European diseases, especially smallpox, killed others. To relieve the consequent shortage of forced labor, the planters bought African slaves.

For nearly forty years no other Europeans seriously challenged Spanish interests in the Caribbean. A series of four Papal bulls issued at the time of Columbus's second voyage had decreed Spain's exclusive right to the area. The only legitimate trade with the West Indies was handled by Spaniards or other nationals licensed by the Spanish government. The colonies, being remote and poor in their early years, attracted little attention.

In the 1530's, Europe took notice of the increasing trade from the West Indies. The islands came to be valued for their products and for the effects that control of them had on the capacity to make war in Europe. More than two centuries of smuggling and raiding ensued. For fifty years the most important economic interference with Spanish control of the Caribbean was carried on by Portuguese slavers not licensed to do business in the Indies. Smuggled slaves became a major source of forced labor for the expanding plantation agriculture of the islands.

French privateers came into the Caribbean in significant numbers in 1536. The English followed during the 1560's. Some of the interlopers came in peace to trade with settlers; others pirated Spanish ships or raided the harbors, either as private enterprise or in furtherance of their countries' political and war aims. The Netherlands took no part in this during the sixteenth century because they were controlled by Spain.

England, France, and later the Netherlands each tried repeatedly to break Spain's hold on the Indies. Their objectives were to deny to Spain the means for making war and to exploit the islands. The standard plan, used over and over with variations, was to capture the major Spanish cities of the Caribbean and hold them with permanent garrisons. England sent Sir Francis Drake, commanding ships of the navy, on such a mission in 1585. He captured the two most important cities in the Caribbean—Cartagena, on the northern coast of Colombia, and Santo Domingo. Each city was held for ransom for a few weeks and systematically looted and destroyed, the townspeople having fled to the hills. Tactical success notwithstanding, the strategic aim of Britain to break the Spanish hold on the West Indies was not achieved. Drake returned to Britain in 1586, and the colonies enjoyed a ten year grace period free from serious harrassment while the fighting went on in Europe. Spain used the time to improve land and sea defences—the monumental forts of San Juan, Puerto Rico, date from this time—so that England's campaign of 1595 was repulsed.

The turn of the century marked great changes for the West Indies as Spain suffered European reverses and the Netherlands threw off Spanish rule. Spain reluctantly gave up her claim to unoccupied lands in the New World in treaties with England and the Netherlands. These two countries and France opened a new era of exploration and settlement of the smaller Caribbean islands, which presently comprise the British Virgin Islands, the United States Virgin Islands, the West Indies (British), the French West Indies, the Netherlands Antilles, Trinidad and Tobago, and Barbados.

England and France were chiefly interested in establishing colonies. The first permanent English settlement in the West Indies was St. Kitts, on the island of St. Christopher, in 1624. A French group arrived shortly after, and both groups shared the island until the English occupied it all in 1702 during the war of Spanish Succession. The whole island is commonly known now as St. Kitts. Englishmen also settled on Barbados later in 1624, and on St. Croix, Nevis, Antigua, and Montserrat in the next eight years. The French established themselves on Martinique and Guadeloupe in 1635.

The Dutch led Europe in shipping and commerce during the seventeenth century. The islands they settled in the 1630's—Curacao, Saba, St. Eustatius, and St. Martin—

served as trading and smuggling depots. Curacao provided salt for the fishing fleets of the Netherlands. Soon after, Aruba and Bonaire also began contributing salt.

Jamaica, least developed of the Spanish islands, was captured by the British in 1650 and settled by British colonists in the 1670's. The larger Windward Islands—Dominica, St. Lucia, St. Vincent, and Grenada—remained unsettled until the end of the century. Earlier English and French attempts had been repulsed by the large numbers of fierce Carib Indians who lived there.

Continuing disputes over ownership notwithstanding, the crowned heads of England, France, and Holland had laid claim to all of the major islands in the Lesser Antilles by the end of the seventeenth century. However, little constructive use was made of them. The three nations gave far greater attention to the North American mainland. In the islands, buccaneers were everywhere, disrupting trade and bedeviling the settlers; and the colonial governors and military leaders fought each other. The planters raised their tobacco and cotton and defended themselves as best they could. Many islands were fought over many times. The richest free port of the Americas, St. Eustatius, changed hands ten times between 1664 and 1674.

In the century's final years, West Indian living achieved a measure of stability. The island governments found the pirates to be unreliable partisans, and with the governments no longer encouraging it, piracy and privateering died out in the Lesser Antilles. A loosely organized group of ruffians continued to pick their living in the Spanish area of the Greater Antilles and Central America. Since most of the pirates were of French or English origin, their work was occasionally commissioned by governments of French or English islands. Though Europe's wars continued to spill over to the Indies, the years between were times of genuine peace.

Small amounts of sugar cane had been raised on some

of the West Indian islands from the early days of settlement, but the final product was too low in quality to be commercially valuable. But the Dutch learned successful methods of growing and milling cane on the South American mainland. Always eager to extend their trade, they began introducing cane to the Lesser Antilles, starting with Barbados in 1637. They supplied capital, milling equipment from Europe, cane from Brazil, and the necessary technical skill. At mid-century, sugar was the only important crop of the French and English islands. It remained one of several crops of the Spanish islands.

The nature of sugar cultivation and the expensive machinery required to mill it called for large scale landholdings and a sizeable labor force that could be driven hard in season. During the eighteenth century, the French and British islands became sites of great plantations where a relatively small minority of Europeans ruled many slaves. Fortunes were made and great fortifications built to protect them. The famed triangular trade route from Europe to African slave ports to the West Indies thrived—a flourishing example of mercantilist theory put in practice. Sugar and slaves dictated the course of economic progress. Island society was organized to meet the needs of the plantation system, and the effects persist to the present.

At the beginning of the nineteenth century the West Indies were busy and prosperous. The islands had command of the European sugar market and, despite the emphasis on sugar, they also controlled the market in cotton and tobacco.

The nineteenth century heralded the diminishing of armed conflict between competing powers in the New World. Dutch interests in North America had been obliterated. England had lost her thirteen colonies in their revolution. The French and British had resolved much of their conflict in North America when France disclaimed her interest in Canada in return for concessions in the West Indies, including the return of Guadeloupe and Martinique to her control.

English domination of the Eastern Caribbean islands was established. Spain also had her islands, and the Dutch were content to maintain themselves as leaders in West Indian commerce.

Peace and prosperity were short lived. Events on the continents and in the islands were conspiring to destroy the economic base upon which the islands depended.

Beet sugar production increased in France during the early 1800's. Interference by American privateers with Caribbean trade during the War of 1812 served to accelerate the development of beet sugar production in other European nations as well. By the end of the war, European sugar production was sufficient to discourage expansion of trade in cane sugar from the West Indies. More than three centuries after its discovery, Cuba finally came into its own as a producer of cane sugar. Its production, greater than that of all the small islands together, was enough to serve the cane sugar market in both North America and Europe. The small islands were unable to compete successfully with Cuba.

To make matters worse, cotton and tobacco were being grown in the southern states of the United States in increasing amounts, and the market in Europe shifted toward that source.

In the Lesser Antilles themselves, prosperity was undermined in more subtle but far-reaching ways. The small islands with precipitous slopes had been intensively cultivated for over a century. Forests had been cleared without thought to protection of critical watershed needs. Consequent erosion and loss of fertility increased the cost of agricultural enterprise.

In addition to increasing costs and the loss of primary markets, the Caribbean's plantation-based economy suffered a final blow.

It was widely believed that the plantations could not survive without slaves. Britain's Parliament passed a law abolishing slave trade in the British empire in 1807. Similar legislation followed shortly in Holland, France, and Spain, but illicit trade between Africa, the Caribbean islands, and the southern United States kept up the supply for a number of years. The planters lived in fear of slave uprisings. Finally, when emancipation laws were passed in 1833 in England and 1848 in France, slavery ended. Abolition came to the Dutch islands in 1863, and to the Spanish in the 1880's.

After the middle of the nineteenth century, the West Indian islands drifted into their most dismal period. North and South American continental interests were established and no longer required supplies or protection from the islands. Much of the soil and forests of the islands had been mined beyond their capacity to produce profitably. The markets for Caribbean products had been won away by larger and more efficient producers. And slavery had been abolished.

From that point, these tiny crumbs of the great colonial scheme rapidly slipped into political and economic doldrums. The old land ownership patterns were changed, estates dissolved, and estate owners returned to their European homelands. Armies and navies were sent to more promising colonial possessions. And the tired land became the heritage of the newly freed slaves.

Three generations passed in which the colonial governments made only feeble attempts at educating, housing, or providing other basic social amenities for the West Indian peoples. It was a time in which populations grew rapidly, and it was a time in which lack of transportation and communication produced an economic and social isolation no less complete than the natural isolation of the islands during past geologic years.

Concern for the islands flared briefly during World War I, and their economic condition improved for the duration. But not until the 1940's—because the world's major political and economic alignments were again disrupted, the normal flow of resources impeded, and more effective means of transportation and communications developed—did concern for the islands truly awaken in Europe and North America.

During World War II, major involvement resulted from the strategic value of the islands. In the post-war years, improvements in West Indian living were continued in response to world-wide pressure for the modernization of social and economic conditions of the less developed parts of the world. In the islands, schools were built, housing improved, and accelerated programs for increasing agricultural production appeared. Transportation and communication were improved, and varying methods were applied to lead the peoples of the islands toward some degree of self-government. Money for these projects was supplied by continental governments.

Concomitant with these activities, there has been an acceleration of private investment from Europe and the Americas. The fledgling oil and petrochemical industries of Curacao, Aruba, and Trinidad were considerably expanded, as were a variety of small industries. The climate of the islands and their proximity to large tourist markets has resulted in a growing tourism industry.

There has been a revitalization of society in the islands due to the combined efforts of West Indian citizens and the metropolitan nations. The pace of island life has quickened. But without a sufficiently reasoned approach to the use of island resources, the price of rapid emergence into the twentieth century may be destruction of the works of nature and the historical record of man, which are themselves an important part of the resources.

III

Social and Economic Characteristics

The governments of the islands are ultimately responsible for controlling the use of natural and historic resources, whether privately or publicly owned. They have the power to hold and administer valued sites, to invest such power in quasi-governmental agencies, and to regulate private actions for the benefit of the general public. Conservation action by governments depends upon their realizing the positive value of such action, and upon effective leadership by administrators and legislators. The democratic nature of the island governments requires that government conservation programs have the approval of the citizenry. Because the desires of the people and their governments are shaped by the social and economic context in which they function, it is appropriate to review social and economic characteristics of the islands in view of their relation to conservation of natural and historic resources. A brief survey of the islands' political status, population, education, and economic conditions follows.

Social characteristics

Political status[1]

Barbados and Trinidad and Tobago are independent nations. The other nineteen islands are politically associated with Great Britain, France, or the Netherlands.

Barbados, formerly a British colony, became independent in November, 1966, and is a member of the British Commonwealth. Its government is a parliamentary one with a House of Assembly established in 1639. Trinidad and Tobago received its independence from Great Britain in August, 1962. It is a member of the Commonwealth and the Organization of American States. Its government is also patterned after the British parliamentary system.

Six Associated States which were formerly British colonial possessions are Antigua-Barbuda, Dominica, Grenada, Montserrat, St. Kitts-Nevis-Anguilla, and St. Lucia. Their new status went into effect during February and March, 1967, following agreement between government ministers of the islands and Great Britain and approval by the island legislatures. The states are entirely self-governing except that Great Britain retains control over their defense and foreign affairs. Any of the Associated States may become completely independent upon its request. On St. Vincent, a British island, the decision to accept or reject the status of Associated State is to be determined by the government after the next national election is held.

The six islands of the Netherlands Antilles are divided into four units of government: Aruba, Bonaire, Curacao, and the Leeward Islands—St. Eustatius, Saba, and the Dutch part of St. Martin. Each unit is governed by popularly elected representatives who legislate on matters pertaining to their respective islands. Representatives are elected from each of the island units to the Netherlands Antilles government, whose capital city is Willemstad, Curacao. This government handles matters pertaining to the six islands and controls the disbursement of revenues deriving from the six islands. The Netherlands retains control over the defense and international affairs of the Netherlands Antilles.

The French West Indies comprise two overseas departments of the government of France: Martinique, and Guadeloupe and its dependencies. Guadeloupe's dependencies include St. Barthelemy, the French part of St. Martin, Marie Gallante, Desirade, and the Isles les Saintes. Just as if the two departments were physically joined with France, they send elected representatives to the French National Assembly and Senate. The administrative head of each department is a Prefect who is a civil servant of the French government.

Population

Overpopulation has long been the undoing of social-economic planning in the Caribbean. In the realm of economic planning, it has compelled the governments of the islands to depend increasingly on hopes for expanded tourism and industry. The agricultural sector is incapable of absorbing the numbers of unemployed people presently living on the islands, and there is little hope that agricultural potentials will provide more employment in the future.

Table 1 shows the total population and population density in 1963 and as anticipated for 1970 in the twenty-two islands. The relationship of the number of people to the small amount of land and the underdeveloped economy poses serious problems, and the substantial population increase expected on all of the islands adds particular urgency to the search for ways to raise standards of living and improve social services.

Birth control programs offer hope of limiting the population increase, but there is considerable cultural resistance to be overcome. E. Gordon Erickson, who conducted demographic and socio-cultural studies in the British West Indies for three years beginning in 1956, described the cultural attitudes toward sex and fertility as "laissez faire."[2]

Fertility generally bears little relationship to the economic condition of a family unit, as it might in many West-

TABLE 1

TOTAL POPULATION AND POPULATION DENSITY OF THE STUDY ISLANDS
IN 1963 AND AS ANTICIPATED FOR 1970[3]

Island	Population Total		Density per square mile	
	January 1, 1963	Anticipated for Jan. 1, 1970	Jan. 1, 1963	Jan. 1, 1970
Guadeloupe (including St. Barthelemy and French St. Martin)	294,000	350,000	432	515
Martinique	300,000	365,000	706	859
Netherlands Antilles	199,607	246,400	507	625
Trinidad and Tobago	889,600	1,090,000	449	551
Antigua (including Barbuda)	56,800	67,000	334	394
Barbados	235,132	282,321	1,416	1,701
Dominica	63,235	73,000	207	239
Grenada	89,377	105,000	672	789
Montserrat	12,507	18,000	368	529
St. Kitts-Nevis-Anguilla	57,000	64,000	380	427
St. Lucia	91,136	101,000	383	424
St. Vincent	85,272	99,000	568	660

ern European or North American cultures. Consensual unions typify the relationship of males and females in the islands, and these are usually short lived. From the male point of view, fertility is sought after as evidence of virility. The West Indian attitude toward fertility is generally permissive, and social approval or sanctions are not usually evident, whether children are born within or without wedlock or whether they come as the result of long lasting or ephemeral unions.[4]

Plans for economic improvement in the islands by government planners are based upon expectations that industrialization and other high employment enterprises will in the main solve the growing problem of overpopulation and consequent high unemployment and underemployment. In the 1962 and 1963 annual reports of the Caribbean Organization, each containing a review of the major points in the development plans of the individual islands, there is no mention of family planning or birth control.[5] The recent *Report of the Tri-Partite Economic Survey* dismisses the subject as being not within the scope of its mandate, which was to suggest short term economic requirements.[6]

Several of the islands have family planning agencies, but on too small a scale to have much effect. The Family Planning Association of Barbados is quite active, and it receives strong government support.

The problem of high population density is intensified by the fact that only about 50 per cent of the total land area is suitable for agriculture.[7] Opening up lands presently held as protected forest would constitute a grave danger with respect to watershed protection. Islands with mountain peaks over 1,500 feet would run the risk of frequent and severe flash flooding.

Providing water and distribution systems to irrigate some of the drier land appears, at best, to be only marginally feasible economically. Changing from cotton or sugar to high profit specialty crops is severely impeded by unfamiliarity with growing and handling such crops, inadequate transportation, and the lack of assured markets.[8]

Expansion of agricultural employment is also limited by the trend toward substituting capital for labor in estate agriculture. World supply and market conditions of the crops typically raised dictate increasing efficiency if the West Indies are to compete successfully. More machinery is needed, not more workers.

Education

Levels of education achievement in the islands are generally low. Most people have only an elementary education, relatively few have completed secondary school, and the number of college graduates is very small. The economic advantages of an educated and skilled population have not in every instance been recognized. W. Arthur Lewis, speaking about the former British West Indies, stated:

> With the exceptions of Trinidad and Barbados, the British Caribbean Islands spend much too little on education, especially technical and university education. . . .
>
> The attitude of ministers especially on the smaller islands is old fashioned, and it would not occur to most of them that investment in education may be as productive as investment in factories or mines.[9]

One of the major obstacles to the establishment of parks, reserves, and historical sites has been the absence of positive feelings on the subject by the public. Public approval and pressure is unlikely to arise unless a significant percentage of the population considers the preservation of nature and the protection and development of historical sites as somehow in their own self-interest. But there is evidence of the relationship of education to interest in nature, history, or archeology on the islands. Aruba, Curacao, Trinidad, Martinique, Guadeloupe, and Barbados seem to have the best developed education systems, and they also have hiking clubs and societies for history, natural history, and archeology.

From the point of view of this study, the role that education may play in fostering appreciation of natural areas and historical sites is important. Elements in the islands' curricula relating to conservation, natural history, and ecology were discussed informally with government officials, educators, and school children. Table 2 summarizes their responses, without claiming to be based on comprehensive investigation. The lack of environmental studies is partially self-perpetuating, because of the limited and inbred nature of the training many of the teachers have had. Results of in-service teacher training efforts tend to be diluted by the constant need for more teachers caused by increasing school age populations.[10]

Socio-cultural research on interest in nature and history as a part of the life styles of West Indians is scarce. A study of this kind was done by Koppel and Carlozzi in Trinidad in 1963.[11] Here one finds some support for the belief that the more education one has, the more likely he is to expand his realms of interest to include activities such as nature study, hiking, and picnicking.

It seems reasonable that knowledge about nature and history promotes interest in places where natural phenomena and physical records of history can be seen, and that the accumulated interest of many people can help secure protection for such places.

Economic characteristics

The economy of each of the Eastern Caribbean islands conforms generally to one or another of six categories. These categories indicate groupings of economic activities as follows: (1) industry, commerce, and agriculture; (2) industry and commerce; (3) agriculture; (4) agriculture and tourism; (5) tourism; and (6) subsistence agriculture and government grants-in-aid.

TABLE 2

OCCURRENCE OF CONSERVATION, ECOLOGY,
AND NATURAL HISTORY IN PUBLIC SCHOOL
CURRICULA OF THE STUDY ISLANDS

| Island | Occurs in the curriculum | |
	Conservation	Ecology and natural history
Anguilla	No	No
Antigua	No	Yes
Aruba	Yes	Yes
Barbados	No	Yes
Barbuda	No	No
Bonaire	Yes	Yes
Curacao	Yes	Yes
Dominica	No	No
Grenada	No	No
Guadeloupe	Yes	Yes
Martinique	Yes	Yes
Montserrat	No	No
Nevis	No	No
Saba	Yes	Yes
St. Barthelemy	No	No
St. Eustatius	No	No
St. Kitts	No	Yes
St. Lucia	No	No
St. Martin	Yes[a]	Yes[a]
St. Vincent	No	No
Tobago	No	Yes
Trinidad	No	Yes

[a]On Dutch part of the island only.

1. Industry, commerce, and agriculture

There is greater economic diversity in Trinidad and Tobago than on any of the other islands. Oil and asphalt have provided the basis for its industrial sector and account for the country's highest value in visible exports. The last decade has brought an increase in industrialization—especially in the manufacture of construction materials, food processing plants, and fabricating industries producing various types of clothing and shoes for the national market and for export. The country serves as an overseas headquarters for numerous commercial houses from Great Britain and other Commonwealth countries that supply West Indian and Latin American markets.

The major agricultural products are sugar, cocoa, and citrus, sold mostly to overseas markets. In addition, a variety of fruits and vegetables are grown for island consumption.

Despite the country's continuing move toward industrialization, and agriculture's diminishing relative importance, agriculture still supplies jobs for approximately 38 per cent of the nation's employed workers. In 1962 it accounted for 12 per cent of the gross domestic product, compared with 18.3 per cent in 1955.[12]

The overall growth rate of the gross domestic product in Trinidad and Tobago has been very favorable. In the nine-year period 1953 through 1961, it increased from $221,000,000* to $552,000,000—an average rate of approximately 16.5 per cent per annum.[13]

Capital accumulation through savings is dominated by government taxation, amounting to 10 per cent of the total national income. Savings by private individuals is nil, and corporate savings equal only 1 per cent of the national income.[14]

In 1958, the government began to control development by means of five-year economic plans. Growing industrializa-

---

*The $ symbol refers in all cases to United States dollars.

tion and consequent urbanization have burdened all public facilities. Heaviest government investments during the period of the first five-year plan, 1959-1963, have been directed toward improvements of the infrastructure.

Tobago, though still a predominantly agricultural section of the country, is influenced by economic changes in Trinidad. Some significant changes in the structure of Tobagonian society can be detected since the 1946 census. The population is becoming urbanized, as in Trinidad. Even more important than the general drift of people from the land to centers of population on Tobago is the migration of Tobagonians to Trinidad. As might be expected in this kind of population movement, the younger people in the labor force are predominant in the group migrating to Trinidad.

There has been a steady decline in the number of people engaged in agriculture on Tobago. Since 1946, the shift has been from agriculture to commercial and service sectors of the economy. This has been partially due to the increase in the tourism industry, but is more an outgrowth of a greatly accelerated public works program. The decline in agriculture has been expressed mostly in a loss of small, independent farmers. The cocoa and copra estates have managed to hold their own during this period of shifting economy and employment. However, present agriculture on Tobago, whether small-independent or large estate, is engaged in mostly by older people.

Tobago's rain forests were one of her most important natural resources. Forest management programs were underway to improve the potential of the forest to support a lumbering industry. But in October, 1963, Hurricane Flora struck the island and leveled most of the forest. The storm was so severe that it also left the few remaining forest stands seriously injured. All efforts to expand the forestry sector of the economy have been abandoned except as the Forest Department may increase its labor force for the purpose of reforestation. The forest as a productive resource is lost for the next several decades.[15]

2. Industry and commerce

Aruba and Curacao are economically distinct from the other islands because of the importance of industry and commerce to their economy, and because they do not have much agriculture. Aruba and Curacao are also relatively wealthy islands. Average annual per capita income is in excess of $900, a very high figure for the Caribbean area. Government income per capita is the highest in the Caribbean at $206 per year.[16]

The chief industrial activity on both islands is oil refining and related petro-chemical manufacturing. The refineries were built originally to refine crude oil from Venezuelan fields, but today they accept crude oil from North America and the Middle East as well. Curacao has deposits of calcium phosphate which are mined and manufactured into superphosphate fertilizer.

Commercial activity is high, in keeping with the islands' historical development. Like all of the Dutch islands in the Caribbean, Aruba and Curacao are duty-free ports. Markets for imported manufactured goods are found throughout the West Indies and Latin America. A lively but unaccounted smuggling trade takes place from Curacao to Venezuela.

Industry, government services, and commerce each make use of about 30 per cent of the employed population on both islands. Agriculture supports less than 2 per cent of the employed population.[17] The arid climate precludes much opportunity for cultivation, though Aruba has made use of hydroponic gardening to the extent that it supplies itself with many fresh fruits and vegetables.

3. Agriculture

Agriculture is the preponderant element of the third economic category, which prevails most often in the Eastern Caribbean islands. Grenada, St. Vincent, St. Lucia, Dominica, Martinique, Guadeloupe, Montserrat, St. Kitts, and Nevis are in this category. Agriculture contributes between 40 and 50 per cent of the gross domestic product of these islands, except in Martinique where the percentage is somewhat lower. In all of the islands, between 50 and 70 per cent of the employed labor force is in agriculture.[18]

Large plantations are still the dominant feature in the agricultural sector of the economy. St. Kitts is the most extreme case, the ratio of independent cultivators to plantation workers being one to seventy-three. Grenada has the lowest percentage of agricultural workers employed on plantations —30 per cent—and agriculture on the island can be characterized as peasant proprietorship.[19] The kind of crops being raised is an important factor in perpetuating large landholdings. Primarily, these are crops like sugar, bananas, and cocoa that lend themselves to more efficient production on larger holdings.

Dominica, St. Lucia, St. Vincent, Guadeloupe, and Grenada have increased banana production in the last decade. The increase has not effectively added to total agricultural output because bananas were substituted for other crops. On St. Vincent, Guadeloupe, and St. Lucia, sugar was the displaced crop, but on Dominica it was citrus orchards.

Guadeloupe and Martinique have the most diversified agricultural production of this group of islands, producing sugar, bananas, cocoa, cotton, pineapples, coffee, and vanilla. Pineapples have become a very valuable crop on Martinique, and increasing acreage is being allocated to them. As with the bananas in the British islands, pineapples generally occupy land formerly devoted to sugar cane.

The agriculture of St. Kitts is the least diversified of these islands. Its production is made up almost entirely of sugar cane. Refined sugar and molasses accounted for about 93 per cent of the visible exports from St. Kitts in 1964.[20]

Montserrat is the least productive of the agricultural islands. At one time, it supplied fruits and vegetables to St. Kitts, Nevis, and Antigua. Today it raises only enough to serve its own market. Efforts were made in 1959 through 1961 to increase tomato production. A small processing plant was built in 1960 to produce tomato purée and tomato paste. But the government's attempts at encouraging the farmers to raise tomatoes failed, due to the inexperience of peasant proprietors in handling this type of crop. Production goals of 40,000 pounds of tomatoes per acre per year were never realized. The farmers were disappointed with the insufficient yield of tomatoes and reverted to the traditional crops of ground provisions, cabbages, and lettuces.[21]

All of the islands of this group are trying to improve their general economic condition, and tourism is the sector on which they concentrate. Grenada has made the largest gains in recent years. In 1962, the value of its income from tourism was equivalent to 47 per cent of total visible exports.[22] St. Lucia's tourism industry is also growing well.

Guadeloupe and Martinique were fortunate in having available the financial and institutional means for developing tourism. The Société Immobilière et Touristique d'Outre Mer, commonly known as SITO, was a tourism development corporation of the French metropolitan government operating in the islands, but it ceased functioning in 1965. Delegates in each of the French overseas departments carried out basic research on tourism, assisted in financing hotels with SITO funds, and administered programs to improve the tourism potential of the departments. On Guadeloupe, two resort hotels, each having over 200 rooms, were opened in 1963. Martinique's SITO program concentrated less on hotel construction and more on enlarging the cruise ship business. Success in this area has enlivened the commercial sector of the economy so that in 1964 it accounted for approximately 32 per cent of the gross domestic product.[23]

4. Agriculture and tourism

Antigua and Barbados are the two islands in the fourth economic category, that of agriculture and tourism. Both islands rely on sugar cane and tourism for the bulk of their economic activity. However, the level of economic activity is much higher on Barbados than on Antigua. Gross domestic product for Barbados in 1964 was $88,000,000, compared with $15,000,000 for Antigua.[24]

Agriculture in general is slightly more important for Barbados, where it contributes 39 per cent of the gross domestic product, than on Antigua, 37 per cent. Sugar and sugar products accounted for 76 per cent of total external trade on Antigua in 1962, while similar commodities made up 68 per cent of external trade for Barbados.[25] Experiments in machine picking and cleaning Sea Island cotton, a long staple cotton grown on several islands, are in progress in Antigua and could conceivably lead to expansion of cotton production there and in other agricultural islands.[26]

Tourism is important to both islands, though clearly more so to Antigua where tourism provides about 39 per cent of the gross domestic product. The figure given for Barbados is 13 per cent. Barbados, like Martinique, enjoys many visits from cruise ships during the tourist season. Income generated from this business is grouped with general retail trade and commerce, and hence is not counted as income derived directly from tourism.[27]

5. Tourism

St. Martin is the only island deriving its major source of income from tourism alone, the fifth economic category. The resort hotels and duty-free shops are the dominant economic factors generated by private enterprise. The island has no appreciable agriculture, though there is a small commercial lobster fishery. Most public facilities and services are provided through allotments from the Netherlands Antilles government.

6. Subsistence agriculture and government grants-in-aid

The sixth economic category, based on subsistence agriculture and government grants-in-aid, includes Anguilla, Barbuda, Bonaire, Saba, St. Barthelemy, and St. Eustatius.

These islands are all characterized by physical and/or climatic factors which make them unsuitable for cultivation. With the exception of Saba, all of the islands receive less than forty inches of precipitation annually, an amount that is insufficient for most crops in the Caribbean. Saba's average annual rainfall is about seventy inches, but the island is too precipitous for cultivation.

St. Eustatius is the only one of these islands ever to have occupied an important economic position in the Caribbean. In the eighteenth century it was the richest commercial center in the Lesser Antilles. Now it ranks with Barbuda as one of the two poorest islands there. Both islands depend upon government grants-in-aid and money sent in by islanders working away from home, either on other West Indian islands or in North America. Agriculture consists mostly of small subsistence gardens. Some cattle and goats are raised on both islands. Meat from the livestock is utilized entirely on the respective islands, and only salted hides are exported. A small amount of charcoal is produced on Barbuda and exported to Antigua.

The economy and quality of living on St. Eustatius have declined steadily since British naval forces destroyed the island's buildings and commerce in 1781. The population that in the mid-1700's numbered over 30,000 has dropped to approximately 1,000. Poor agricultural methods and the prolonged raising of cotton have caused serious erosion damage still in evidence and have resulted in the destruction of the soil moisture balance. Consequently, the island has slowly dried out during the last 300 years. Only a few wells remain, and these are at sea level, producing nothing but brackish water. Potable water supplies are obtained entirely from cistern-captured water from the roofs of houses. The hilly land of the northern third of the island seems to have been less affected by the poor farming practices of the past, and today could probably support a modest beef cattle enterprise. The island is in serious difficulty with regard to employment. Most income is derived directly from the government. Public works expenditures are very low, offering only sporadic part-time employment.

With the exception of Bonaire, all of the islands in the subsistence agriculture and grant-in-aid category are political wards or dependencies of other governments in the Caribbean. Economic statistics are usually not available for these islands, since they are commonly grouped with the overall statistics from the parent island. Characteristically, the islands in this group suffer from a lack of communication with the other islands in the West Indies and with the mainland countries.

Bonaire gives the impression of being the most prosperous of this group, though its prosperity is to a great extent illusory. The condition of public services and facilities is high, but this is mainly due to large public works expenditures subsidized by the Netherlands Antilles government. Tourism is stronger on Bonaire than on any of the other islands in the group and supplies about 70 per cent of the gross domestic product. Agriculture on the island consists of cultivating aloes and raising goats.

In general, tourism has been the one feature that all the islands in this category have tried to encourage. Small hotels (less than twenty-four rooms) have been built on all of the islands except St. Eustatius, and local tourist boards or committees administer promotion campaigns. People on the islands admit these efforts have not been very successful. Lack of transportation and communications, unskilled populations, and most significantly a lack of sufficient investment capital to provide competitive resort facilities and ancillary services have combined to frustrate the efforts of the islanders.

Conclusion

The people of the islands would like to have a full share of the benefits of modern living. The island governments are aware of their responsibility to improve components of modern existence such as education, health care, streets, water and sewage systems, electricity, and telephones. However, progress toward these ends is slowed by inertia engendered by too many years of stagnation and hampered by shortages of money and skills. The governments are eager to support development proposals offering solid hope of advancement. But when development plans call for destruction or significant alteration of valuable natural or historical sites, there is reason to ponder the consequences. One golden egg has value, but should a goose be killed?

IV
Caribbean Flora and Fauna

The natural vegetation

Descriptions of the vegetation of the islands by Columbus and early settlers indicate that at the time of settlement all of the inner arc of volcanic islands was virtually covered by a mantle of rain forest. The mature rain forest is a fascinating emotional and visual experience, especially for someone accustomed to the forests of the temperate regions. As P. W. Richards, an authority on tropical forests, says, "Few writers on the rain forest seem able to resist the temptation of the 'purple passage'."[1] Even Columbus succumbed, describing the forests of Hispañola:

> Its lands are high and there are in it very many sierras and very lofty mountains, beyond comparison with the island of Teneriffe. All are most beautiful, of a thousand shapes, and all are accessible and filled with trees of a thousand kinds and tall, and they seem to touch the sky. And I am told that they never lose their foliage, as I can understand, for I saw them as green and as lovely as they are in Spain in May and some of them were flowering, some bearing fruit and some in another stage, according to their nature.[2]

Tropical rain forest is always very green. Trees, clean

boled, tall, and slender, predominate almost to the exclusion of shrubs and herbs. Lianas (woody vines) cascade out of the forest canopy and hang 100 feet to the forest floor. Epiphytes such as orchids, ferns, and bromiliads cling tenaciously to branches and stems. Variety seems endless, sufficient to humble the most determined of botanists.

The tropical forest is not an impenetrable jungle in the popular sense. Only where the canopy is opened and sunlight reaches the forest floor does undergrowth become dense enough to impede walking. The rain forest is humid and temperatures are warm the year around. Trees have growth forms that appear strange on first observation. Some flowers and fruits arise directly from tree trunks. Buttressed roots, flaring from tall trees, need only a roof spanning the capacious enclosure between to make a rude hut. Most trees bear colorful and conspicuous flowers, though it requires a lot of looking up to see them high in the crowns.

There is no equivalent of tropical rain forest in the United States. Only the southern-most tip of Florida is in the true tropical climatic region, but the vegetation of this area is a coastal swamp type that bears little resemblance to rain forest. For most North Americans, the Caribbean islands afford the closest opportunity to experience the special enjoyment of the tropical forest and to study its biology.

In contrast to the green lushness of the mountainous rain forest islands are the coral capped islands, where low rainfall and seasonal rainfall patterns have created completely different vegetative formations. Scrub and brush, often described as thorn forest, predominate in the landscape. True tropical desert can be seen in areas of Aruba, Curacao, and Bonaire. Typically, thorny trees with miniscule leaves are interspersed with cacti. Along windswept coasts, sea spray driven inland has evaporated, leaving a crystalline patina of salt on the bare soil between plants. On Anguilla, Antigua, Barbuda, and St. Barthelemy, where rainfall is seasonal, the scrub forest is deciduous. Shades of brown, yellow, and gray characterize the landscape during the dry season. Only coastal vegetation is green all the year.

Taken as a whole, the Caribbean islands present a variety of tropical plant communities. Some are widely distributed, such as mangrove swamps and coastal woodland. These consistently express the combined effects of the climate and land touching sea. Some communities, such as the desert plants or the elfin woodland of the highest mountain peaks, are expressions of climatic extremes.

The phyto-geographical spectrum that has resulted from the combination of climatic, geological, and evolutionary events in the Lesser Antilles has been described by Beard in the classification system which appears in Table 3.[3]

The distribution of plant species on the islands conforms with the relative differences in age of the islands. Thus, the oldest islands (Martinique, Dominica, and Guadeloupe) have the largest number of species and the largest number of endemic species—species that evolved within and are restricted in range to a particular area. Endemic species are concentrated among the highland flora. According to Beard, nearly half of the highland flora of the three oldest islands is endemic. Lowland flora has a much lower rate of endemism. Beard offers this difference as evidence supporting the thesis that a land bridge existed between the islands of the Lesser Antilles during the Miocene epoch.[4]

Howard divides the plant species of the Lesser Antilles into categories ranked in order of the number of species in each category:

(1) species found in the Lesser Antilles and in the Greater Antilles but not in the South American flora, (2) species endemic to the Lesser Antilles, (3) insular endemics, (4) species found also in South America but not in the Greater Antilles, and finally (5) species of cosmopolitan distribution. The categories rank in about the order given.[5]

The large variety of endemic species found in the Caribbean is of special interest to biologists studying the proc-

TABLE 3

CLASSIFICATION OF PLANT COMMUNITIES[6]

Primary climax communities	*Secondary and sub-climax communities*
A. Climatic Climax Formations	
1. Optimal Formation:	
Rain Forest	Tree-fern brake
	Miconia thicket
	Pioneer forest
2. Montane Formations:	
Lower Montane Rain Forest	Symphonia swamp
Montane Thicket	Palm brake
Elfin Woodland	Pioneer communities of
	volcanic ejecta
	Fumarole vegetation
3. Seasonal Formations:	
Evergreen Seasonal Forest	*Acrocomia* bush
Semi-Evergreen Seasonal	Cactus bush
Forest	Logwood thicket
Deciduous Seasonal Forest	Logwood-Acacia bush
	Thorn savanna
	Fire grasslands
	Leucaena thicket
	Cordia thicket
	Croton thickets
4. Dry Evergreen Formations:	
'Dry Evergreen Forest'	
Evergreen Bushland	Thorny thickets
Littoral Woodland	Vegetation of sand-dunes,
	salt flats, rock pave-
	ments, and rocky slopes
B. Edaphic Climax Formations	
5. Swamp Formations:	
Swamp Forest	
Mangrove Woodland	
6. Seasonal-Swamp Formations:	
Savanna	

esses of evolution, genetics, and ecology. The islands provide a natural laboratory setting because they are separated from each other and from mainland tropical areas. The basic biological events on each island can go on with minimal influence from outside areas.

The description of the floristics and plant geography of the Lesser Antilles is open to much conjecture and leaves many major questions still unanswered. For example, the earliest comprehensive cataloging of Lesser Antillean flora was done by Grisebach from 1859 to 1864.[7] His work and all subsequent accounts were necessarily after the fact of the major period of exploitation of land on the islands. Therefore, that highland forests today exhibit the highest amount of endemism and lowland flora are the most cosmopolitan may be simply a reflection of the pattern of land use. Highland flora was and still remains the least disturbed, while lowland flora was and is most subject to human activity, including the possibility of transfer of plant species from one island to another.

Most of the original plant communities of the islands are no longer present. Three and one-half centuries of agricultural activity have dramatically altered the plant formations so that climatic climax communities—plant communities which are the culmination of natural growth in a given climate—are found only in the most isolated and inaccessible portions of the islands. The greatest loss has occurred on Barbados, which at the time of settlement was over 50 per cent forested and today is 0.05 per cent forested. Denudation of the forest for agricultural purposes has affected Dominica least of all, 75 per cent of the land being forested as late as 1952.[8]

Extensive alteration in the islands' natural vegetation occurred from the middle of the seventeenth century to the end of the eighteenth century. This was the period of greatest activity in opening up lands for cultivation. Sugar, more than any other crop, was responsible for the reduction of forests. Sugar required large acreages for economical cultivation, and the refining process required large quantities of fuel, almost all of which was supplied from local forests.

In the middle of the nineteenth century when the Caribbean agricultural economy entered a period of decline, much of the land that previously had been cultivated reverted back to some form of natural vegetation. Today, except on Barbados, the islands are less extensively cultivated than they were during the eighteenth and early nineteenth centuries.

Over three hundred years of grazing by livestock, especially goats, have changed the character of natural communities on most of the islands. This has been particularly true on the islands which have drier climates originally supporting seasonal and dry evergreen formations and are unsuited to the raising of cultivated crops.

The most prevalent form of climax community presently found on the islands of the Lesser Antilles is elfin woodland, typically occupying the highest peaks and the most inaccessible terrain. Throughout the islands, secondary and sub-climax communities predominate. Undisturbed stands of rain forest are found only on Guadeloupe, Dominica, St. Vincent, and Trinidad. Undisturbed montane formations other than elfin woodland are equally rare. Undisturbed seasonal or dry evergreen formations are present only on the island of Barbuda. Climax formations resulting from soil conditions have probably suffered less than any other types in the region. Most of these are in very moist or swampy lands that were undesirable for agricultural purposes and often a health hazard because of insect-carried diseases.

In spite of the losses of the past, there is still much to be learned about the islands' tropical vegetation. Where virgin forest stands exist, their grandeur and beauty are part of a valuable heritage for the Caribbean people. But this heritage and the opportunity to study it are jeopardized by an absence of effective conservation laws and practices.

The fauna

Because of their geological youth and their isolation from the continents, the Caribbean islands have never had an abundance or variety of animal life. Birds and reptiles predominate in both numbers and kinds over the other vertebrates. Mammals, amphibians, and freshwater fish are scarce.

Lizards are seen from the centers of cities to the heart of the forest, they occupy every strata of the forest from tree tops to forest floor, and they live in every climatic zone from the wettest parts of the moist tropics on Dominica to the deserts of Aruba. Chameleons, gekkos, anolids, and iguanas —colorful, swift, and acrobatic—are the ubiquitous animals of the islands.

There are more kinds of birds than reptiles, but the birds are not as readily visible. Except for a few species of thrushes, flycatchers, doves, finches, and honeycreepers that are adapted to human activity, birds are rather inconspicuous in the landscape. The parrots of the Windward Islands and the flamingoes of Bonaire are the only bird species remaining that satisfy the conception of spectacular tropical bird life. However, few people ever see the parrots, for they live in the tropical forests of the high mountains where only the most persistent searchers go.

The bird life of Trinidad is exceptional. Having once been part of South America, Trinidad shares in some of the richness of the continent's bird life.

Mammals native to the islands are scarce. Bats are among the very few endemic mammals that preceded man to the islands. There are other mammals, of course, but their appearance among the island fauna is either recorded in the list of post-Columbian introductions or lost in the undeciphered records of aboriginal life and the events of evolution.

The mongoose is one introduced mammal that can be easily found on most islands. Monkeys, agouti, and armadillo brought from Africa, Trinidad, and South America have lived for several centuries on some of the islands, but like the parrots they are seen only in the more remote parts of the forest.

The vertebrate animals have suffered as discouraging a history as the flora of the region. J. H. Westermann, of the Foundation for Scientific Research in Surinam and the Netherlands Antilles, summarized the unfortunate story of the extinction of animal species in his review of the literature on the destruction and preservation of flora and fauna in the Caribbean area.[9]

Comparable data regarding the time span during which extinction is reported to have taken place are not available for all classes of vertebrates in the region. Westermann finds documentation on extinct mammals covering a time span of almost 2,000 years, a time span of 300 years for birds, and 100 years for reptiles and amphibians.[10] He lists 87 species or subspecies of vertebrates that have become extinct in the Caribbean region, including 41 mammals, 21 birds, and 25 reptiles or amphibians. Most of the extinct animals were insular endemics. Regional endemics have survived due to their wider range and the fact that human influence has not been uniform on all islands. In the islands of the study group alone, 21 species or subspecies of animals (4 mammals, 10 birds, 7 reptiles or amphibians) have suffered extinction. At the present time, 36 species or subspecies are threatened with extinction (5 mammals, 16 birds, 15 reptiles or amphibians). The factors which have played a major role in the loss of these species are: (1) the destruction or degradation of essential habitat, (2) the introduction of alien, predatory species, and (3) direct exploitation such as hunting.[11]

Parrots *(Amazona)* and macaws *(Ara)* have been the most severely reduced groups of birds. These large and colorful birds were sought after for meat, plumage, and eggs. The clearing of forest land in combination with hunting probably brought about the extinction of five species of parrots and macaws among the islands of Martinique, Guadeloupe, and

Dominica. So thorough was their destruction that not even one preserved study specimen exists. Two species of wrens *(Troglodytes)* and nightjars *(Caprimulgus)* have been lost from the Leeward Islands, and a large finch *(Loxigilla)* from St. Kitts.

The four parrot species of the Windward Islands are presently threatened with extinction. Having suffered a severe reduction in their forest habitat, they now reside in the few remaining stands of mature rain forest on their islands. The endemic parrot of Bonaire is similarly threatened by change and loss of environment as well as human predation. Only the protective action of one landholder, who owns a large area where the parrots live, impedes the final extinction of this bird.

The large birds of the swamps, such as spoonbills *(Ajaia ajaja)*, limpkins *(Aramus guarauna)*, and the West Indian tree duck *(Dendrocygna arborea)*, have long been prized for sport and meat, and are in a precarious position today.

The rodent family suffered the only recorded extinctions among the mammals of the Lesser Antilles. Martinique, St. Lucia, and Barbuda have witnessed the extinction of their native species of muskrat *(Megalomys)*.

The fruit-eating bats *(Ardops)* of Dominica, Guadeloupe, St. Lucia, and Montserrat are living precariously and, like the parrots, could become extinct with further reduction of their forest environment.

Of the reptile species lost, most were lizards. The mongoose is the agent of destruction frequently blamed for their loss. The survival of the large genus of ground lizards *(Ameiva)*, with representative species on most of the islands, is an example of how man has inadvertently contributed to the protection of animals. Only in the villages and cities where mongoose refrain from going do these interesting ground lizards persist.

Snakes have been persecuted relentlessly and, as in the rest of the world, many species have been lost that do no harm to man but are often directly beneficial to human interests because they prey on destructive rodents and insects. The mongoose has assisted in the reduction and disappearance of many snake species. The boas *(Epicrates)* and constrictors *(Constrictor)* have suffered on all the islands. The black snakes *(Alsophis)* were particularly susceptible to the predations of the mongoose.

The animals native to one island were particularly susceptible to extinction because their populations were small and they were adapted to life in very restricted habitats. Endemic species that have survived the intensive exploitation of the islands are generally animals associated with habitats found in the highland forests.

The mongoose has been the most devastating of the animals imported to the islands. It was brought to the West Indies during the 1800's for the purpose of controlling the imported black rat, an animal that was especially destructive to sugar cane. The mongoose adapted readily to the island environment, but its feeding habits were not confined to the intended prey. It became a predator on all accessible forms of mammals, birds, reptiles, and amphibians.

Other introduced predators have contributed to the extinction of native fauna. Feral dogs and house cats as well as monkeys have been effective in reducing the numbers of endemic animals. The green monkey *(Cercopithecus sabaeus)* is believed responsible for the extermination of the St. Kitts bullfinch *(Loxigilla portoricensis grandis)*.[12]

As might be expected, the eighteenth and nineteenth centuries were the most disastrous years for the animals of the islands in the study group. Since the decline in estate agriculture, the immediate threat to animal life has been somewhat mitigated. However, surviving species such as the parrots have often had their habitat greatly reduced, and their tenure is a precarious one.

The reduction in the amount of land cultivated has not produced a corresponding return to the original forest types that provided the habitat for most of the regional and insular endemic animals during earlier periods. While there is more wild land today than there was at the close of the nineteenth century, this represents, in the main, secondary formations that have developed on abandoned agricultural lands. The senior author found no significant areas where succession on abandoned agricultural land had even approached the condition of optimal rain forest which was the predominant formation at the time of European settlement. The intensive cultivation of steep, highly erodable slopes and the disturbance of the soil and water complex have reduced the capacity of the land to support montane forest and other lower montane primary communities. There has also been considerable increase over the years of flocks of goats and sheep that graze and browse upon the vegetation and have retarded the process of succession over extensive areas.

Natural catastrophes, primarily volcanic eruptions and hurricanes, have undoubtedly played their part over the years in reducing populations if not causing the extinction of animal species. Records describing the extent that hurricane damage may affect the populations of animals on the islands are not available. Hurricane Flora, which struck the island of Tobago in October, 1963, caused between 80 and 90 per cent destruction of the forest over almost the entire island.[13] What effect this might have upon the population of fauna on the island is an area that offers prime opportunities for research.

The 1902 eruptions of Mount Soufriere in St. Vincent and Mount Pelee in Martinique produced local but completely devastating effects upon the natural landscape. The effect of these eruptions upon the fauna of the islands is a matter of conjecture, for no records of zoological research following the eruptions are to be found.

Considering the limited number of vertebrate animals found in the Caribbean islands, the record of extinctions and presently threatened species is appalling. Nearly 40 per cent of the world's recorded extinctions by humans or human agents have occurred in the Caribbean.[14] The unhappy condition of the endemic species remaining resulted from acts of past generations, but the continued survival of these species depends upon today's people.

Nature preservation laws[15]

Since the turn of the twentieth century, some efforts have been made to protect the fauna and flora remaining on the islands from further depredations and destruction. At the present time, all of the islands studied have legislation in effect designed to protect completely certain types of flora and fauna or to control exploitation of others. Unfortunately, except for Trinidad and Tobago and the Dutch islands Aruba, Curacao, and Bonaire, laws pertaining to the protection of fauna are largely unenforced. Preservation of flora has come about largely through establishment of forest reserves or their equivalents for the purpose of safeguarding watersheds. Grenada, St. Vincent, and Barbados have legally established nature sanctuaries giving complete protection to natural vegetation.

With three exceptions, laws protecting plants and animals were enacted after 1900.

Laws protecting fauna

The first law specifically relating to the preservation of fauna in the British West Indies was enacted by Grenada in 1891. It is interesting to note that the classes of fauna protected by this first ordinance are birds and fish. Mammals, reptiles, and amphibians were not included in this or any subsequent law on Grenada or on any but three of the other islands in the British West Indies.

St. Vincent was the next British island to promulgate legislation, with a birds and fish protection ordinance in 1901. This was followed by similar ordinances protecting birds on Montserrat in 1912, Dominica in 1914, and St.

Lucia in 1916. In most cases, the laws applied to species in the following orders: Columbiformes, Psittaciformes, and Passeriformes (Mimidae). Birds in these groups have been commonly hunted for sport and meat throughout the history of the islands.

Only three laws have been enacted protecting classes of vertebrates other than birds and fish in the British islands. The Crapaud Ordinance of 1939 in Dominica provides protection for the frog *Leptodactylus fallax*. The black fish *(Globicephala melas),* a whale, was protected by the St. Vincent Whale Fishery Ordinance of 1925 which established seasons and licensed whalers. This ordinance has since been repealed. Barbuda controls the taking of deer *(Odocoileus)* through hunting regulations. These regulations are not statutory. They emanate from the office of the island warden (administrator).

Enactment of laws in the Netherlands Antilles for the protection of fauna occurred in 1926. Protective laws apply solely to birds and the deer *Odocoileus gymnotis curassavicus.*

The first wildlife protection laws in the study islands were enacted for Guadeloupe and its dependencies in 1859. These ordinances regulated the taking of game (species unspecified) with respect to seasons. In 1928, an ordinance was passed protecting most species of Passeriformes that were believed beneficial to agriculture.

Martinique first enacted laws protecting fauna in 1927. These laws regulated the taking of species sought after for sport or meat. As in the case of Guadeloupe, the species were unspecified and the laws regulated only hunting seasons. Martinique is the only island studied that protects the mongoose. The mongoose protection ordinance was enacted in 1914. Despite the damage to poultry and many forms of wildlife, this ordinance is still in force because it is believed that the mongoose effectively controls the fer-de-lance snake *(Bothrops atrox),* the island's only poisonous reptile.

The Wild Animals and Birds Ordinance of 1933 was

Trinidad and Tobago's first law protecting fauna, excluding opossums, bats, squirrels, rats, mice, agouti, and mongoose. Species hunted for sport and meat (deer, armadillo, peccary, herons, ibis, waterfowl, rails, shore birds, and pigeons) are protected by closed seasons and bag limits. The country has two nature sanctuaries established specifically to protect two species of birds. Caroni Sanctuary in Trinidad protects the nesting area of the scarlet ibis *(Eudocimus ruber)*. Little Tobago Island, lying about one mile offshore from the western end of Tobago, was designated a national bird sanctuary in 1948 to preserve an introduced colony of New Guinean birds of paradise *(Paradisia apoda)*.

Protection of flora

The oldest protected forest in the Caribbean, King's Hill Forest Reserve, was established in 1791 on St. Vincent. All vegetation is protected from exploitation, and the reserve also serves as a nature sanctuary. On Grenada, the Grand Etang Forest and Water Reserve, established by statute in 1906, offers complete protection for all plants and animals within the reserve. Turner's Hall Wood on Barbados was declared a nature sanctuary by legislation, though the Wood remains in private ownership. For its 1966 independence celebration, Barbados acquired Farley Hill Woods and, by administrative decree, established Farley Hill National Park. The Barbados National Trust purchased Welchman's Hall Gully in 1962 and developed the area as a protected site of botanical and scenic interest.

In 1912, St. Vincent proclaimed that forest lands above the altitude of 1,000 feet were to be reserved forest for the purpose of watershed protection. Similar ordinances establishing forest reserves were enacted by St. Kitts-Nevis-Anguilla in 1903 and 1927, Montserrat in 1946, Antigua-Barbuda in 1941, Dominica in 1946, St. Lucia in 1945, and Grenada in 1949. In all cases, regulations pertaining to the forest reserves are concerned with keeping the forest generally intact rather than offering complete protection to all forms of vegetation. Forest reserves are commonly subjected to grazing and some harvest of timber and shrubs for construction materials and fuel.

The Netherlands Antilles has no legislation pertaining to protection of forests or vegetation.

Forestry legislation in the French West Indies is a part of the metropolitan government's Forestry Code which went into effect on January 1, 1948. Forest reserves such as found on the British West Indian islands do not exist in the French islands. However, the Forestry Code does serve to regulate the use of the forest to the extent that watershed values are maintained.

Forest ordinances passed by the Trinidad and Tobago governments in 1916 and 1918 established the present system of forest reserves for the major purpose of protecting watersheds.

National parks

There is a marked scarcity of conservation laws establishing national parks and equivalent areas in the islands. The national park concept is a relatively recent idea in the world. In terms of world-wide acceptance, it is essentially a product of the last forty or fifty years. As a device for ensuring that people can continue to enjoy and study nature's activities, it has proved itself in many nations under a variety of legal-institutional forms. Certainly the concept of protecting a portion of the landscape so that the normal processes of nature can occur without human interference is as valid for the islands as for the continental nations. The colonial administrations of the past clearly did not set many effective precedents on the islands in this area of conservation. We are hopeful, as the era of colonialism is ending in the Caribbean, that the new nations there will view the establishment of national parks and reserves as a desirable expression of national concern for the natural and historic wonders over which they now have full stewardship.

PART TWO

The Inventory

LOOKING OUT ON A MOTHER OF CACAO TREE FROM THE
INTERIOR OF THE RAIN FOREST

V
The Inventory

The inventory presented in the next three chapters lists more than 120 sites of natural or historical importance. These sites are the resources that provide much of the richness in the islands' landscapes. They contain basic material on which the study and understanding of natural processes depends, they are some of the visible aspects of national identity, and they provide opportunities for recreation and education for the people of the islands and tourists.

Our purpose in compiling this inventory is to show the extent and variety of natural and historical sites scattered throughout the islands. Though some islands are more richly endowed than others, each one has something to offer.

The importance of preserving natural areas was emphasized at a conference on Neotropical botany held in 1962 at the Imperial College of Tropical Agriculture, St. Augustine, Trinidad. The conference recommended that "each country of the Neotropics work toward a system of natural area reservations that will include examples of all of the principal landscape types and their associated natural vegetation and animal life."[1] It was the feeling of the biologists at this conference that such reservations could play a critical role in the development of the islands and countries of the Neotropics.

The primary orientation of the scientists attending the conference was toward the value of such areas as outdoor laboratories for scientific study. However, the potential of these areas to serve recreation needs was not ignored, for the conference also recommended:

> . . . that scientists favour compatible public uses of nature reservations—as for recreation in the North American, British and Finnish sense—while guarding zealously such protection of nature as is needed for research and education, now and in the foreseeable future.[2]

In accordance with the conference recommendation, our inventory includes representative samples of the major types of plant communities, as described by Beard.[3] However, rather than choose examples of all the plant communities on each island, we have chosen sites on an area-wide basis. Duplication of primary or secondary formations appearing in the inventory occurs because variations exist within each basic type of formation as one moves from one island to another. For example, rain forest on Montserrat is not quite the same as rain forest on Martinique or St. Vincent. Also, interest in the preservation of fauna associated with the various plant communities makes it necessary to duplicate the selection of vegetation types on different islands. For instance, four endemic species of parrots *(Amazona),* birds of the mountain forests, appear on three different islands: Dominica, St. Lucia, and St. Vincent. To preserve the remaining populations of these four parrots, it is necessary to establish nature reserves in the rain forests and montane forests on each of those islands.

In general, attention was given to the selection of plant communities, as we believe the needs of the animal populations will be served best by guaranteeing the existence of a diversity of habitat types. While this is by no means a complete answer to the preservation of fauna, it certainly is the soundest ecological basis for building a program of protection.

The need for underwater parks to preserve the fauna and flora of marine communities is relatively new. The improvement of SCUBA and snorkeling equipment during and after World War II has led to an increasing number of people becoming interested in observing the natural phenomena of marine communities. In addition, scientific investigations and oceanography have been intensified in the last two decades. Being in large part scientific pioneers, marine biologists have a strong desire to see samples of primary marine communities set aside and protected so that they may be studied in an unaltered state. The coastal reef communities included in the inventory are those which seem most interesting in terms of variety of plant and animal species, size, and apparent lack of disturbance or alteration by man.

Background information relating to public recreation in the islands is scarce, because there is a lack of government involvement with it. Plans for public recreation areas were rarely available. Statements relating to the selection of sites for public recreation use that appear in the inventory are based upon the authors' observations of the patterns of outdoor recreation on the islands. Beaches, by far the most popular natural areas for outdoor recreation, were selected for the inventory on the basis of their intrinsic qualities and the need of any given island for recreation areas regardless of the quality of its beaches as compared with other islands. Characteristics considered desirable were sand of light color and fine texture, absence of heavy surf, clear water, and seasonal stability of the beach.

The importance of white sand beaches is an additional reason to preserve the coral reefs to which they are ecologically related. Reefs are the major source of material for white beach sand. Consequently, beach protection should include protection of reefs offshore and along adjacent headlands.

Investigations of historical sites covered evidences of the pre-Columbian aboriginal cultures and remnants of post-Columbian settlement, with special effort directed toward the identification of important buildings and fortifications which are in serious need of restoration or in imminent danger of being destroyed or degraded through adverse forms of land use and vandalism.

It was difficult to proceed very far with investigations into the location of Amerindian sites in the Lesser Antilles. There has been little systematic, professional research carried out on the twenty-two islands studied except in the Dutch Leeward Islands, St. Lucia, and to a limited extent Trinidad and Tobago. Where prior studies have been conducted, we drew on them for general background and to locate the archeological sites for the inventory.

The historical buildings and fortifications mentioned in the next three chapters seem outstanding, both in their structural qualities and in their roles in Caribbean history. Many appear to be threatened by proposed land use changes or accelerating disintegration through weathering.

The rain forest islands are discussed, in alphabetical order, in Chapter VI; the seasonal forest islands in Chapter VII; and the tropical desert islands in Chapter VIII. At the beginning of each of these chapters, there is a table showing the kinds of sites found on each island. As the islands are taken up in turn, beach and marine sites are discussed first, followed by inland natural areas, wildlife, and historical and archeological sites. On islands where there are not sites in every class, the same order is used but the inapplicable classes are omitted.

VI
Rain Forest Islands

The rain forest islands make up the inner, volcanic arc of the Lesser Antillean chain. Precipitous mountain peaks, forests green through all seasons, and agricultural fields are the major elements of the landscape, and most of the resources of natural and historical interest relate to them. The moist, tropical climate and rich volcanic soil provided the basis for the islands' economy from the time of settlement to the present. Agriculture and use of the forest for fuel and timber began at the bottom of the mountains and proceeded upward until only the mountain peaks and swampy areas remained in their natural state. Eventually, nature imposed her own restrictions, and men were driven back down the steep slopes by erosion, floods, and loss of soil fertility.

Secondary forests have regenerated on most of the abandoned land, but they lack the splendor of the virgin rain forest. Pockets of unaltered forest on most of these islands suggest the beauty that confronted the first European settlers.

In addition to forest communities of plants and animals, the rain forest islands contain a variety of other natural features, such as volcanic sulphur springs, crater lakes, a petrified forest, swamps, and beaches.

Because men valued the wealth these islands could pro-

TABLE 4
RAIN FOREST ISLANDS

Island	Beach and Marine Areas	Inland Natural Areas	Wildlife	Historical and Archeological Sites
Dominica		Forests	Parrots	
Grenada	Beaches	Crater lake Forests	Monkeys	Forts
Guadeloupe	Beaches	Volcanic sulphur springs Forests		Forts
Martinique	Beaches	Area displaying plant succession Petrified forest Forests	Birds	St. Pierre museum Forts
Montserrat	Beaches	Volcanic sulphur springs Forests Waterfall		Church Sugar mill Fort

Island	Coastal	Natural features	Animals	Historic/cultural sites
Nevis	Beaches Fringe coral reefs		Monkeys	Alexander Hamilton's birthplace
Saba		Forests		Fort
St. Kitts		Forests	Monkeys	
St. Lucia	Beaches	Forests Soufriere	Parrots	Fort Government buildings
St. Vincent	Beaches	Crater lake Area displaying plant succession Forests	Parrots	Petroglyphs
Tobago	Beaches Patch coral reef		Birds of paradise Game animals	Fort
Trinidad	Beaches	Tropical acid bog Forests Swamps Pitch lake Waterfall and pool	Oil birds Scarlet ibis Monkeys Game animals	Mansions National Museum Fort

duce, the history of the islands is rich in tales of war and trade. Forts, government buildings, commercial houses, and plantation great houses survive, reminders of times past.

Dominica

Dominica is the only island in the Lesser Antilles with a significant amount of relatively unaltered forest, and in the forest live two endemic species of parrots.

Especially fine examples of virgin rain forest, lower montane rain forest, and elfin woodland are on Mount Diablotin in the north-central part of the island. To the south, in the Trois Pitons area and the Soufriere Hills, there are a swamp phase of the montane thicket and fumerole vegetation, in addition to the communities mentioned above. The swamp phase of montane thicket is unique among the islands of the Lesser Antilles.

The imperial parrot *(Amazona imperialis),* an endemic species threatened with extinction, occupies the high peak areas of Mount Diablotin and its connecting ridges. The red-necked parrot *(Amazona arausiaca),* also endemic, lives in the forests of Mount Diablotin at lower elevations.

In spite of the logging which took place in the eighteenth and nineteenth centuries, Dominica affords the best opportunity for an extensive forest park and ecological study area in the Lesser Antilles. However, protective measures must be taken soon. In April, 1967, the government of Dominica negotiated a contract with a lumber company allowing timber to be cut from previously protected crown-lands and forest preserves. If widespread commercial use is made of the mature forest on these lands and reserves, the world stands to lose two unique and beautiful bird species and an uncommonly good source of ecological information about the tropical forests of the eastern Caribbean.

Grenada

Grenada has interesting beaches, a crater lake in a forested area, monkeys, and old forts and barracks.

Grand Anse is the only large, white sand beach in Grenada. Located south of the capital city of St. George, the beach is about two and one-half miles long and excellent in quality. There are many very small beaches between the fringe of headlands along the south coast of Grenada. A narrow peninsula at Point Saline is bordered on the east by a white sand beach and on the west by a beach made of black volcanic sand. Seasonal evergreen plants cover the higher land behind the peninsula. The scene is one of interesting contrast in the Grenada landscape.

A crater lake called Grand Etang lies in the central massif just south of the mid-point of Grenada. Approximately 3,500 acres of forest land around the Grand Etang has been established as a forest reserve and wildlife sanctuary. Most of the forest in the reserve is rain forest or lower montane rain forest. The ridges of the surrounding peaks—Morne Quaqua (2,412 feet), Mount Sinai (2,300 feet), and Southeast Mountain (2,359 feet)—are covered with a mixture of palm brake (*Euterpe* sp.) and elfin woodland. Within the rain forest there are enclaves of palm brake and tree fern brake *(Cyathea),* sub-climax communities located on old landslides.

Most of the forest land around Grand Etang and all of the other high elevations of the island were badly damaged by a hurricane in 1956 which resulted in the loss of many trees in the emergent, or top-most, layer of the rain forest. Second growth that includes cabbage palm (*Euterpe* sp.) and trumpet trees *(Cecropia)* is common. With the canopy opened after the hurricane, the undergrowth has become quite lush, and the ground is covered with moss, bromiliads, aroids, and thickets of lobster claw *(Heliconia).*

Mona monkeys *(Cercopithecus mona),* native to the Cameroons in western Africa, have become naturalized, and several small troops of these monkeys are in the Grand Etang area. Westermann suggests that they were possibly introduced to the island by slave traders.[1]

No exploitation of the fauna or flora is allowed in the Grand Etang Forest Reserve and Sanctuary, which is Crown Land under the jurisdiction of the Grenada Forest Department. Island residents and tourists visit the Grand Etang. A system of trails had been cut and several scenic lookouts provided, but they were destroyed or damaged by the hurricane and have not been rebuilt. The Grenada government constructed two houses near the crater lake, one serving as the residence of forestry officials and wardens, and the other as a guest house providing rooms and meals.

Fort George is the largest of five historic military installations overlooking St. George. Built by the French during their occupation of the island in the mid-1700's, the fort stands on a high bluff on the northern point of the entrance to St. George's harbor. The other four installations occupying the top of the north-south ridge just east of the city are Fort Adolphus, Fort Lucas, Fort Frederick, and the old barracks. They are all owned by the government but have not been officially designated as historical sites. Fort George serves as a police station, and the old barracks area has been remodeled, in part, to provide quarters for nurses resident at the hospital.

Guadeloupe

The island of Guadeloupe consists of two large bodies of land with only a narrow land connection between them. Basse Terre is the western part of the island, and on it are high mountains with virgin rain forest and a sulphur volcano. Grande Terre, the eastern part, has a number of very fine beaches. Forts are located on both sections of Guadeloupe.

The beaches of Grande Terre are all located on the southern coast. Almost all of them have white or very light brown sand and, being on the leeward coast, provide excellent swimming throughout the year. The best beaches are located in the crescent bays between Gosier and Sainte-Anne and from Saint-Francois eastward to Pointe-des-Chateaux. A small hotel near Gosier offers change houses and showers to the public for a small fee. It is the only facility of its kind in Guadeloupe.

La Soufriere and Sans Toucher are the highest mountain peaks on Guadeloupe, with elevations of 4,870 feet and 4,855 feet. The highest parts still retain some excellent stands of virgin rain forest. La Soufriere is the site of a sulphur volcano and hot springs. The volcano itself is considerably larger than the one on Montserrat (page 66) though the area influenced by volcanic action covers only about one-third that of Montserrat, or about two and one-half acres. The mountain peak area of La Soufriere and Sans Toucher abounds in small waterfalls and scenic cascades scattered through four distinct vegetation communities—rain forest, elfin woodland, lower montane rain forest, and seasonal evergreen forest. The Department of Forestry is responsible for the management of forests in the area, which is publicly owned. The Mountaineering Club of Basse Terre maintains a series of footpaths for hiking to the top of La Soufriere. Close to the summit, the club maintains a small rest house which was built to serve their own membership but is used now to some extent by tourists.

Fort Fleur de l'Epee is about midway between Pointe-a-Pitre and Gosier, on the southern coast of Grande Terre. It was built in 1763 by the French in order to guard the entrance of the bay and channel leading to the docks at Pointe-a-Pitre. Most of the outer walls of the fort remain intact, though almost all of the interior buildings except the powder magazine have disintegrated or been pirated by the local people to acquire cut stone.

Fort Richpance, built in 1692, served as the main protection of the city of Basse Terre, the capital and early port city for Guadeloupe. The fort is about twice the size of Fort Fleur de l'Epee and is built in the same style as Fort St. Louis in Martinique. It has been maintained in good condition throughout its history, mostly because it has been used continuously by the French military.

A program to restore Fort Fleur de l'Epee was initiated in 1963 by the delegate to Guadeloupe of SITO (Société Immobilière et Touristique d'Outre Mer), a French government corporation whose purpose was to assist France's overseas departments in improving their tourism industries. Restoration of the outer walls is nearly complete and a brief mimeographed history of the fort has been made available for visitors, but in the meantime SITO itself has ceased to exist.

Scientific studies have been carried out on a continuing basis by scientists and historians resident in the French West Indies and from France. Père Pinchon, of Martinique, has been active in studying the fauna of Guadeloupe as a part of his work to create a series of books on the fauna of the French Antilles. The first book, on birds, was published in 1963.[2]

Martinique

A variety of inland natural areas and an outstanding fort are major attractions of Martinique, one of the few islands in the Lesser Antilles that has resident academicians of high standing. The president of the Natural History Society, Père Pinchon, has conducted ecological and biological studies of the French Antilles for over thirty years. M. Petitjean-Roget, president of the History Society, has been studying the history of the French Antilles for over twenty years. Numerous scientists, historians, and archeologists from France have visited the island throughout its history as a French possession. The Forest Department is active, with a staff made up of five professionally trained foresters who administer the forest lands owned by the government, conduct forest research, and maintain several experimental plantations.

Martinique has numerous small crescent beaches along its southeast and south coasts. They are all light or medium brown sand of about the same texture and quality as the beaches of the north coast of Puerto Rico. The best of Martinique's beaches are located toward the southern end of the island, particularly at Point Baham and St. Ann. Diamant Beach, at the western end of the south coast, is a beach of good quality, though it tends to have more surf than the others because there is little offshore protection by reefs.

There is very little development of beaches on Martinique, except at Diamant Beach and a new public beach development at Trois Ilets. In both instances, the local government is responsible for maintenance and operation of the facilities and beaches, though initial development costs are underwritten by the departmental government in Fort de France.

Mount Pelee, the volcano that erupted in 1902 and buried the town of St. Pierre, marks the highest point on Martinique—4,800 feet. The mountain supports a fine example of plant succession dating from the eruption. The pattern of successional communities is similar to that on Soufriere Mountain in St. Vincent (page 72). Most of the Mount Pelee forest area is in public ownership and is managed by the Department of Forests. Although there are no officially designated parks or nature reserves on Martinique, the Tourist Office in co-operation with the Department of Forests has established and maintains a series of hiking trails through the Mount Pelee forest land. Maps of the area are available, and directional signboards with maps have been placed where the trails cross highways or roads. The Department of Forests maintains several small picnic areas in its experimental mahogany plantations on the Mount Pelee slopes. Apparently, the trails and picnic areas are used most by tourists.

Some timber is harvested throughout the private and government owned forest areas, though the wood products industries on Martinique are very small. The present system of logging seems to have no detrimental effect upon the natural communities of the forest land.[3]

Pieces of petrified wood, branches, and trunks of trees are scattered over approximately five acres of petrified forest, about thirteen miles south of Vauclin on the southeast tip of Martinique. Petrification apparently took place beneath the sea. Since the mineral replacement of the original wood is almost entirely calcium, the petrified wood does not present the array of attractive colors that occurs when petrification takes place in fresh water. However, this is the only area in the West Indies where there is petrified wood in quantity and size. Though privately owned, the area is open to the public. It is accessible only by foot.

Midway along the east coast of the island, the Caravelle Peninsula juts out about eight miles into the sea. The peninsula is one of the most scenic areas of the island. The numerous precipitous rocky headlands of the coastline and the many small islands offshore are particularly attractive. The eastern end of this peninsula is almost entirely vegetated and is the home of many species of land and sea birds. The members of the Martinique Natural History Society hope to obtain the eastern end of the Caravelle Peninsula as a bird sanctuary and park, but they have refrained from seeking donations of land from the individual owners because the Society is without sufficient funds to develop the area or to provide it with adequate protection.

A moderate amount of wild pigeons and doves are shot in the Caravelle Peninsula during the hunting season each year, but apparently no particular danger exists to the nesting flocks of these birds.

Fort St. Louis, built in 1668, is the oldest fortification of any size south of Brimstone Hill in St. Kitts. It was built by the French to guard the harbor of Fort de France, and is so constructed that the outermost walls rise from the floor of the bay. The fort is in relatively good condition, having been used continuously as a French military installation throughout the years that the French have had control of the island. However, little attention has been given to the value of most of the fort as an historical site, and no effort has been made by the military to preserve the early armaments or to return them to their original emplacements.

Approximately one-fifth of Fort St. Louis is under control of the History Society of Martinique. This part of the fort was opened as an historical site for about one and one-half years. Due to lack of operating funds, the Society was forced in 1963 to shut down its operation and disband the small zoological park that they had located inside the fort in co-operation with the Natural History Society. The History Society remounted many of the original guns and returned them to their emplacements, cleaned up the interior of the fort, and undertook small scale restoration of some of the partially disintegrated ramparts and tunnels.

The History Society of Martinique is very interested in reopening Fort St. Louis as an island historical site. They have plans for developing two small museums in the fort when it is opened—one to cover pre-Columbian cultures and the other to display materials pertaining to the history of the fort itself. Unfortunately, after spending more than $30,000 on the fort in the past several years, the Society's treasury is exhausted.[4]

Martinique's old capital city of St. Pierre was completely covered by volcanic ash and lava when Mount Pelee erupted in 1902. Part of the city's ruins have been excavated by the Municipality of St. Pierre, the new capital city. The ruins and a small museum of artifacts uncovered during the excavation are still being worked on by the local government. An admission fee (about $.50 U.S.) is charged of visitors to the museum, presumably to cover maintenance costs. The museum is neither well laid out nor in very good condition.

Montserrat

Volcanic sulphur springs, elfin woodland, a waterfall, and ruins of a church and sugar mill are all located in a mountainous area in the south of Montserrat. The island also has several beaches and ruins of a fortification.

Montserrat's beaches are almost entirely dark brown or black sand. The largest, Plymouth Beach, extends from the northern edge of Plymouth village to the outlet of Sand Ghaut Creek. This southwest coast beach is completely in the lee and is excellent for swimming. Other beaches of good quality are at Woodlands Bay, Carrs Bay, and Little Bay along the west coast of the island, north of Plymouth. The only light sand beach is at Rendezvous Bay, about eight miles north of Plymouth. Since there is no road to Rendezvous Bay, access is gained by taking a boat from Plymouth or by driving the twelve road miles to Little Bay Beach, where small boats can be chartered to go around Rendezvous Bluff to the beach. The other beaches can be reached by road or path and are easily available for recreation. The local population makes some use of them. Although the beaches from mean high tide to the water's edge are public, all beach frontage is privately owned.

Volcanic sulphur springs known as Galway's Soufriere are located about midway up the south slope of Chance's Peak (3,000 feet), the highest mountain on Montserrat. The soufriere is the largest of several on the island, and the largest and one of the most active in the West Indies. The soufriere area encompasses approximately seven and one-half acres where the activity of many steam and sulphur geysers permits virtually no vegetation to live. The general atmosphere is one of utter desolation, a stark contrast to the tropical forest through which one travels to reach it. The main volcanic activity comes from a single, continuously active geyser hole about fifteen feet in diameter. Eruptions from it reach about six feet in height. Numerous small hot springs discharge steam and boiling water.

The ecological effects of the soufriere are in evidence over a much wider area. Sulphur fumes driven by prevailing winds have influenced the vegetation of the surrounding slopes to the extent that no trees are present. Ground cover is bromiliads (especially *Pitcairnia*), *Philodendron gigantum*, ferns, and a few shrubs (*Clusia* spp.).

On the northeast slope of Chance's Peak Ridge is one of the finest examples of elfin woodland in the Leeward Islands. Mr. Kingsley Howes, former Conservator of Forests and an experienced naturalist, reports that the Chance's Peak elfin woodland contains the greatest variety of elfin woodland species in the Leeward Islands.[5] The tree hibiscus (*Hibiscus tulipiflorus*) is unusually abundant there. The total area of this community has never been determined, but the senior author judges it to be about 1,000 acres. Access to the woodland is very difficult, because there are no trails and the slopes are very precipitous.

At Great Alp Falls, between Galway's Estate and Fergus Mountain Estate, the White River cascades approximately ninety feet into an attractive plunge pool surrounded by lush vegetation. There is no convenient access to the falls at present, the only route being a very poorly kept foot path along the White River Gorge.

Approximately one and one-fourth miles north of St. Patrick's Village, along the road to Galway's Soufriere, are the ruins of the earliest church built on Montserrat. The exact date of its construction is apparently unknown, though several local people who have studied the history of Montserrat suggest the 1640's. Some 150 years ago, the church was abandoned and acquired by the owners of Galway's Estate for conversion to a sugar warehouse. Surrounding the church are ruins of the sugar refinery and windmill. The estate is still privately owned.

The ruins of the only significant fortification on Montserrat are located on Fort St. George's Hill, about one and one-half miles northeast of Plymouth. The major ramparts and breastworks were constructed from earth and rock and have eroded badly. Twelve of the original cannon are still on the hill, though they have long since been removed from their original emplacements. The only masonry structures built at the fort were two powder magazines. One is intact, but the other has disintegrated to the point that only parts of two walls remain standing. About three and one-half acres of Fort St. George's Hill encompassing the immediate site of the fort is publicly owned. A recent island administrator, Mr. Donald Wiles, provided for maintaining the unpaved road to the top of the hill and clearing a small amount of brush so that visitors may walk about on the site of the old fort. A few people go there for picnics, though it is not developed for that kind of use. The Tourist Board, formed in September, 1963, has indicated that it would like to develop the Fort St. George site as an historical site and public park area. However, no funds are available to the board for doing any of this work.

Nevis

Nevis has several large, light sand beaches between Cades Point and Charles Town on the west coast of the island. Fringe coral reefs follow along three-fourths of the shoreline. As in other fringe reefs in the Leeward Islands, the dominant coral form is elkhorn coral *(Acropora palmata)*. Brain corals of several species are also found in abundance.

Nevis peak rises steeply from the sea to a height of about 3,000 feet. The very top is almost always covered by a ring of clouds, and the resulting vegetation is elfin woodland. The second growth montane and rain forests midway down the slopes are notable only for the population of green monkeys *(Cercopithecus sabaeus)* which they support.

The dilapidated remains of the house where Alexander Hamilton was born are in Charles Town. Only parts of the outer walls and the main staircase are left standing. Owned by the government, the house is tacitly accepted as an important historical site. The Tourist Board counts it among the attractions of the island and has put up a sign identifying

the house and presenting a brief history. Tourists visit it
regularly.

Saba

Drs. Westermann and Stoffers include the four primary
forest communities of Saba Peak in their surveys of the natural history and resources of the Netherlands Antilles.[6] An
elfin woodland of outstanding quality covers the top of the
mountain. The area of the woodland is smaller than on
Montserrat, but the community of bromiliads, climbers, and
epiphytes in it has reached a higher development than on the
other Leeward Islands. Stoffers lists thirty-five species among
this segment of Saba's woodland flora.[7] Below the elfin
woodland, concentric belts of palm brake *(Euterpe)* and
fern brake *(Cyathea)* ring the mountain. A small enclave of
virgin rain forest is on the north side of the mountain.

Residents and visitors sometimes hike up the foot path
to the peak to see the forest and the elfin woodland, but the
government makes no effort to improve or otherwise maintain the trail. The land of Saba Peak is privately owned, in a
multiplicity of small parcels.

St. Kitts

St. Kitts is one of the two Leeward Islands, the other
being Nevis, on which it is possible to find monkeys. But St.
Kitts is best known for an impressive historical site, the Fort
on Brimstone Hill.

Colonists introduced green monkeys *(C. sabaeus)* to
St. Kitts during the eighteenth and nineteenth centuries. One
group of monkeys lives in the northern end of the island in the
forest of Mount Misery. This mountain is the highest on St.
Kitts—4,314 feet. Its peak is covered by an elfin woodland
and palm brake forest common to most of the high peak areas
in the Leeward Islands.

The low hills to the south of Frigate Bay, in southern
St. Kitts, also contain monkeys. In contrast to the mountain

forest, the habitat in these hills is semi-arid bush land dominated by thorn trees and cactus.

The Fort on Brimstone Hill is the most spectacular fortification in the islands south of San Juan, Puerto Rico. Brimstone Hill, the core of an extinct volcano, was first fortified in 1690. The fort was added to several times beginning in 1736, and largely completed by 1782. Except for Nelson's Dockyard in Antigua, there is probably no other fortification as important historically in the Lesser Antilles. The Fort on Brimstone Hill played an important part in many naval battles fought off the coast of St. Kitts during the 1700's and early 1800's, when the island was under contention by Britain and France.[8]

Currently, the fort receives more visitors than any other place on the island. The St. Kitts Historical Society, which administered the fort until recently, covered the costs of a minimal amount of maintenance by soliciting donations from visitors and selling small, illustrated booklets about the fort. The Historical Society attempted to stabilize disintegration of the fort and planned to restore certain portions of the battlements and officers' quarters which have been pirated over the years by people seeking cut stone for foundations for homes. Brimstone Hill is now owned and managed by the Society for the Restoration of Brimstone Hill, a quasi-public corporation chartered in April, 1965. The society is empowered to raise funds and receive gifts of money or property for the purpose of maintaining and restoring the fort, and to publish any material it thinks will help promote its interests.

St. Lucia

An endemic parrot species and an outstanding historical area are features of special interest on St. Lucia.

The best of St. Lucia's beaches are on the leeward coast at Vieux Fort, at the southern end of the island; Grand Cul-de-sac Bay and Vigie Bay, near Castries; and Gros Islet

Bay, on the northwest tip of the island. None is outstanding by Caribbean standards. The sand of the beaches ranges in color from light brown to almost black. The beach-front land along Cul-de-sac and Gros Islet Beaches is mostly privately owned. The Cul-de-sac Bay area is being developed as a site for vacation and retirement homes. Most of the land bordering Vigie Beach is publicly owned, though a small hotel pre-empts access to part of the area.

St. Lucia's only example of montane rain forest is in the high peak area of Mount Grand Magasin and Mount Gimie (3,145 feet), a region of Crown Land under the jurisdiction of the Conservator of Forests. The area has been logged over and cleared, but scattered among the second growth forest are several large remnants of virgin vegetation, especially on the Mount Gimie peak. The forest on Mount Gimie is also the last area on St. Lucia where the St. Lucian parrot *(Amazona versicolor)* lives. This species, which once ranged over all of the forested land in St. Lucia, has been pushed back to its present restricted range by logging and agricultural activities.

The mountainous region is not used much for recreation, and only ill-kept footpaths are available to hikers. Tourists frequently visit a small soufriere near the base of Mount Gimie which can be reached by automobile.

One of the outstanding historical sites in the Lesser Antilles is on Morne Fortune, about three-quarters of a mile south of Castries overlooking Castries Bay. The buildings and fortifications span the years from 1678 to 1911. Included among the structures are ramparts and breastworks, gun emplacements, powder magazine, jail house, officers' quarters, stables, barracks, and administration buildings. Depending upon age and the quality and kind of construction, the structures range in condition from almost completely disintegrated to functionally intact. The buildings on the hilltop are scattered over about seven and one-half acres of turf, with a few trees widely spaced through the area.

The cable and wireless company uses one of the old administration buildings for its transmitting station, and the United States Peace Corps occupies an old barracks as quarters for its female personnel. Morne Fortune is Crown Land. Its use and disposition can be determined by executive and/or legislative action of the St. Lucia government. The Friends of Morne Fortune Association for the Preservation of Places of Historic Interest or Natural Beauty, founded in 1966, is a quasi-public corporation interested in Morne Fortune and other valuable sites. The association proposes to compile a photographic record of valued sites, expand public awareness of their value and beauty, and help preserve them.

St. Vincent

St. Vincent's Soufriere Mountain is not only a scenic attraction but a botanical one as well, for it displays a successional series of natural plant growth. The island also has an endemic parrot species and petroglyphs.

The only white sand beach on St. Vincent is at Tyrells Bay. It is well protected due to its location on the south coast, where it is in the lee of the wind, and the several small islands immediately offshore. Along the west coast there are numerous small, dark sand beaches on small alluvial plains at the mouths of the many rivers between the steep, rocky headlands characteristic of the coastline. The best of these beaches are at Lomans Bay, Mount Wynne Bay, Keartons Bay, and Richmond Beach. Land fronting all of these beaches is in private ownership. Public access to the beaches is allowed by the landholders except at Tyrells Bay, which is operated as a private swimming and boating club. Outdoor recreation is centered on the beaches, but there are no facilities common to public recreation areas.

Soufriere Mountain is one of the most unusual places in the Lesser Antilles. The mountain, located in the northern end of St. Vincent, is a volcano more than 4,000 feet high.

The most recent eruption occurred in 1902. A crater lake about two-thirds of a mile in diameter occupies the cone. The eastern walls of the crater rise above the lake almost vertically for over 1,000 feet. The walls the rest of the way around the lake are much less steep, and not as high. Most of the plants inside the crater are ferns, grasses, or club moss *(Lycopodium)*.

Vegetation on the outside of the volcano represents a successional series of natural growth which has appeared since the last eruption of the volcano destroyed the previously existing forest. At the top of the cone's exterior, the vegetation is reminiscent of alpine tundra, with lichens growing in the stony ground. The lichens (species not identified) appear in two dominant forms, one a light, silvery gray and the other orange. The massed effect of these plants produces a most unusual and appealing landscape.

From the "tundra" formation down to the 2,700 foot contour, vegetation still resembles the alpine. The ground is thickly covered with many forms of lichens, but other plants are scattered throughout. They include grasses and sedges, *Lycopodium*, and ferns. The silver tree fern *(Cyathea arborea),* which on the lower slopes reaches a height of twenty feet, is here seldom more than knee high.

The tree line on the slopes of the cone is reached at about 2,200 feet. Most vegetation between this level and about 1,800 feet is windswept and stunted. In many areas there are large patches of fern brake covered entirely by *Cyathea*. True secondary forest grows below 1,800 feet to about 1,200 feet. The forest is very dense, with stems rising to eighty or ninety feet. The ground is covered luxuriantly with ferns, *Lycopodium, Anthurium,* and a large amount of lobster claw *(Heliconia)*.

The main territory of the endemic St. Vincent parrot *(A. guildingii)* is the Morn Garu Mountains, just south of Soufriere Mountain. The highest point in these mountains is Richmond Peak (3,523 feet). Palm brake covers the mountains, but there are small patches of elfin woodland on the tops of the highest peaks. In general, the slopes on the western side of the mountains are extremely precipitous, while on the eastern side they are more gently graded. Almost two-thirds of the trees are cabbage palm *(Euterpe)*. The southern part of the Morn Garu range is flanked on east and west by rain forest, much of it in patches. The highly erodable slopes are incapable of supporting a mantle of vegetation requiring several decades of stable soil surface in order to form. Scattered patches of virgin rain forest are on the western slopes.

Almost all of the land comprising the Soufriere Mountain and Morn Garu peak area is in forest reserve, maintained for watershed protection by the Conservator of Forests of the St. Vincent Agricultural Department. There are trails through most of the reserve area and to the crater lake. The trails are in poor condition and suitable only for persons capable of rigorous hiking. The tourist board considers the crater lake to be one of the attractions of the island.

The King's Hill Forest Reserve, established in 1791, is the oldest protected forest in the Caribbean. It consists of fifty-five acres of seasonal evergreen forest. All vegetation is protected from exploitation. The reserve also serves as a nature sanctuary.[9]

Petroglyphs are carved in rocks at three locations on the west coast of St. Vincent: at Chateaubelair, approximately one mile upstream from the mouth of the Petit Bordel River; at Layou, about two miles upstream from the mouth of the Rutland River; and at Young's Island, just off the coast at Tyrells Bay. Young's Island is Crown Land. However, the government has negotiated a lease with hotel interests for the transference of the island to private control for the purpose of erecting a resort hotel. The Chateaubelair and Layou petroglyph sites are privately held, but public access is permitted.

Tobago

The coral reef and quiet water of Buccoo Bay are a

showplace of tropical sea life, and the hills of Tobago, where little forest remains, testify to the power of a full-blown tropical storm.

Between sea and land, Tobago has many good beaches, especially on the southwest coast at Great Courland Bay, Little Courland Bay, Buccoo Bay, and Store Bay, and on the southeast coast at Bacolet Bay and Rockly Bay. Another beach of very good quality is at the northern end of the island at Man of War Bay, near Charlotteville. Store Bay and Rockly Bay are publicly owned, under the jurisdiction of the local Tobago government. The narrow strip of land between the shoreline highway and the beach at Rockly Bay is provided with several picnic tables and benches. The beach is much used by residents of Scarborough. Store Bay has palm thatched beach umbrellas and a small change house. One-third to one-half of the beach front land at Great Courland Bay and Man of War Bay is publicly owned. Beach frontage at the other locations mentioned is all privately owned.

Buccoo Reef is about one-half mile offshore at Buccoo Bay. It is an extremely large patch reef built primarily of elkhorn coral *(Acropora palmata)* and brain corals *(Diploria* and *Colpophyllia)*. The reef is large enough to act in many respects as a barrier reef to the Buccoo Bay area. Between the reef and the beach is a very shallow lagoon, four to six feet deep, of exceptionally clear, quiet water and with bottom material of almost pure white coralline sand. Several private boat owners operating out of Buccoo Bay provide guided tours to the reef for snorkelers. Buccoo Reef is designated as an underwater park in which harvest of fish, corals, and other invertebrates is discouraged. However, no statutes protect the reef.

Hurricane Flora flung herself across Tobago in October, 1963, and in the process destroyed 80 to 90 per cent of the forests throughout the island, except at the northern tip, where approximately 50 per cent of the forest was destroyed. Nearly all of the former forest land, about 70,000 acres, is

Crown Land classified as forest reserve under the jurisdiction of the Conservator of Forests. Management of the reserve was directed primarily toward watershed protection. Hunting in the forest for wood pigeons, agouti, and armadillo, a popular sport on Tobago, has been curtailed due to storm-reduced game populations and the difficulties of traveling among fallen trees. Mr. Hollis Murray, Conservator of Forests, has estimated that about thirty years will pass before anything resembling the previously existing forest will have been regenerated.[10]

About one mile offshore from Speyside, Tobago, lies Little Tobago Island, or Bird of Paradise Island. New Guinean birds of paradise *(Paradisea apoda)* were introduced there in the early 1900's, and a small breeding colony of the birds has established itself. In 1948, the island was turned over to the Trinidad and Tobago government for a national bird sanctuary. It has been controlled by the Forest Department since then, and is given complete protection against all forms of exploitive use. It is visited by local people and tourists. Hurricane Flora, which destroyed so much in Tobago, also wreaked havoc on Little Tobago. About half of the birds of paradise and half of the natural vegetation were destroyed, including many of the food-producing plants upon which the birds of paradise depend. Estimates of the number of birds of paradise remaining on the island range from twelve to fifteen.[11]

Trinidad

The landscapes of Trinidad are remarkably varied, for there are mountains, plains, swamps, and even a large pitch lake. In addition to plant communities and animals common to the Lesser Antilles, the island also contains a number of South American species.

In conjunction with the increasing urbanization and industrialization of Trinidad, the people are expanding their interest in outdoor recreation activities. Studies required for a major land use zoning plan were carried out by the Town and Country Planning Division of the Five Year Plan Office during 1963 and 1964, with the help of three planning missions supplied by the United Nations Development Program. The enabling legislation for Trinidad's planning program authorized planning of public recreation areas, natural areas protection, and national historical sites. A plan for a park and recreation system was drawn up for the government with the assistance of the American Conservation Association, Incorporated.

The public lands used most for recreation are park and recreation savannahs (playing fields) and public beaches, especially Mayaro Bay, Maracas Bay, and Las Cuevas Bay. Public recreation areas in the cities and towns are administered by the county councils. Development and maintenance policy emanates from the councils, but construction and maintenance work is done by the Public Works Ministry.

Maracas Bay is presently the major area for bathers in the Port of Spain region, but the bay is only moderately good for swimming because it is not protected by offshore reefs or islands and the surf is frequently very heavy. Located on Trinidad's north coast, about twelve miles from Port of Spain, the beach is about one-half mile long, with brown sand. The beach at Las Cuevas Bay is about one and one-half miles east of Maracas Bay and equal in quality. However, dense vegetation to the rear of the beach promotes a problem of mosquitoes and sand flies. A new highway runs along the north coast to Maracas and Las Cuevas Bays, and the Tourist Board has constructed a small change house and a pavilion at Maracas Beach. Lifeguards are stationed at the beaches, but nothing else enhances the quality of these sites as public recreation areas.

A most promising area for public recreation and swimming is at Balandra Bay, on the east coast just north of the village of Matura. The bay contains about one-fourth mile of brown sand beach that is completely protected to the north and partially protected to the northeast. Surf is present only during stormy periods. Near the small fishing village of Blanchisseuse on the north coast there is a group of small beaches, two of which are in sufficiently protected small bays to afford relief from the surf.

The Aripo Savannah, located approximately four miles southeast of the city of Arima, encompasses about 12,000 acres of land dominated by second growth brush and young forest, which is maintained in an open savanna condition by fire and grazing. One particular area in the savanna stands out as unique among the islands treated here. This area of about twenty-five acres is best described as a tropical acid bog. The conditions producing the high acid situation are not unlike those responsible for northern bogs of glacial origin, but the subsoil is underlaid by precipitated hardpan instead of the clay of northern bogs. Drainage both through the soil and over the surface is retarded by the dish-shaped character of the land. Extensive accumulations of partially decomposed plant materials make the soil almost purely organic. The partial decomposition of the accumulated plant remains by anaerobic breakdown produces the high acid soil condition. The flora of this area is characterized by acid-tolerant hydrophytic plants, including insectivorous forms such as pitcher plant *(Sarracenia)* and sundew *(Drosera)*.

Nariva Swamp, covering 18,000 acres about midway along the east coast of Trinidad, is unique in this group of islands because it is a fresh-water swamp. The area supports some of Trinidad's last remaining populations of macaws, howler monkeys, and a small Trinidadian cayman. The swamp has three basic plant communities. The swamp grass community *(Cyperus giganteus)* is most extensive. Scattered throughout the swamp on areas of higher ground are patches of palm forest made up of cabbage palm *(Raystonea)* and moriche palm *(Mauritia)*. In addition, there are small areas of forest not unlike the rain forest of the mountains. Included are some scattered communities of crappo-guatecare and mora forest. Nariva Swamp also produces conditions very favorable for the development of mangrove trees *(Rhizophora* and *Avicennia)*. Near the mouth of the Nariva River, mangrove achieve eighty feet in height. A Rockefeller Foundation Virus Research Laboratory is located at Nariva Swamp, which is a center of yellow fever and other insect vectored diseases.

Caroni Swamp is an extensive mangrove swamp with a total area of about 14,000 acres, just south of the city of Port of Spain, on the deltas of the Caroni and Blue Rivers. Its most notable asset is the large population of scarlet ibis *(Eudocimus ruber)*. The ibis, previously extirpated from the island, made a re-appearance about twenty-five years ago and has since built to a population believed to be in excess of 10,000 birds.[12] The species was chosen as the national bird and appears on the Trinidadian coat of arms. At low tide, the scarlet ibis wade in the tidal flat areas feeding upon small molluscs, crabs, and other crustaceans. Unfortunately, the populations of crustaceans and molluscs are diminishing due to pollution from a large rum plant that discharges the waste products of rum manufacture into a series of open ditches which drain into the swamp.

The Caroni area also supports substantial breeding populations of shore birds, egrets, herons, and other wading birds, and is a resting and feeding area for migratory waterfowl.

Trinidad's only wildlife sanctuary is located in the Caroni Swamp. The size of the Caroni Sanctuary fluctuates according to administrative decisions based upon the nesting requirements of the scarlet ibis flock. Caroni Swamp, exclusive of the part set aside as a sanctuary, is used during the season for hunting shore birds; wading birds, including the scarlet ibis; and migratory waterfowl. Trips through the sanctuary can be arranged with the Forest Department and have been growing increasingly popular with tourists.

In the highest peaks of Trinidad's northern range and in two or three very small areas in the Nariva Swamp there are communities of crappo-guatecare forest *(Carapa, Esch-wilera,* and *Pentaclethra).* The occurrence of this particular kind of rain forest is limited to these portions in Trinidad and a few isolated areas on the South American continent. Wherever it is located, crappo-guatecare forest has never been known to occupy extensive areas.

One of the most striking trees in the Neotropics is the mora *(Mora excelsa).* Mature specimens sometimes grow to a height of 150 feet. The tree is a shallow rooting one supported by high, flaring buttresses. The ecology of the mora forest is unusual in the Neotropics in that the mora tree seems to thrive in relatively pure stands, as opposed to most tropical forests where up to thirty or forty species of trees per acre are typical. The largest of Trinidad's three mora forests is in the Mayarol region in the southeast corner of the island. Originally, there were approximately 100 square miles of mora forest in this region. There are also stands of mora at Matura, in the northeast corner of the island, and a small area in the Irois region of the southwestern peninsula.

The mora tree has been harvested heavily over the years because it is a desirable timber tree and can be cut efficiently and profitably, due to the purity of the mora stand. The mora forest at Mayaro has been reduced to about one-fifteenth of its original size in the past thirty years. In recent times, as access roads have been extended into the Matura region, the mora forest there has been cut at an ever increasing rate. There is some question today whether the mora trees on the island can be saved. The ecology of this species is so poorly understood that no one knows what the minimum size stand must be in order for the forest to perpetuate itself.

The Aripo Massif is a mountain peak area about twelve miles north of Arima, just west of the Blanchisseuse Road. A remarkable feature of this area is the presence of four caves that support a population of oil birds. It is also an area of outstanding rain forest and lower montane forest, including one of the crappo-guatecare stands. Elfin woodland is found on the peak.

The Blue Basin is a plunge pool below a 100 foot waterfall at the head of the Diego Martin Valley, about six miles north of Port of Spain. The waterfall and pool are set in lower montane forest. The site is administered by the Tourist Board of the Trinidad government. Development of the area is limited to maintaining a footpath and a small part of the shoreline of the Blue Basin where people can enter to go swimming.

Maracas Falls is situated in one of the finest lower montane rain forests on the island, about eight miles north of Tunapuna, at an elevation of approximately 2,200 feet. The falls is inaccessible except to a reasonably determined hiker. The distance from the end of the road out of the village of La Veronica is not great (about one-half mile), but the path is precipitous.

The Trinidad Forest Department, in the Ministry of Agriculture, is responsible for administering public lands designated forest reserves, game reserves, or sanctuaries. All of the areas mentioned above are publicly owned except for one of the oil bird caves in the Aripo Massif. Approximately 60 per cent of the land in Trinidad is publicly owned, and about half of that land has been established as forest reserve, where the Forest Department carries out a program of forest and watershed management. Indiscriminate harvesting of trees is being increasingly controlled by the Forest Department. There is a restriction against cutting any tree with a girth of less than five feet breast high. A cause of considerable damage to the forest lands and their related watersheds is burning of the forest for amusement.[13] It is done during the dry season when the lowland forests are especially susceptible. The northwest section of the island near Port of Spain has suffered repeated damage of this sort, and as a result streams emanating from the mountains in this area are subject to frequent flash flooding.

At the present time, none of the reserve land is being managed for recreation purposes, but it is open to such public recreation as may take place in the absence of administration or development. There is informal use of the numerous small streams throughout the interior of the island for swimming. However, none of the streams is developed or maintained for this purpose. The Forest Department has established eight game reserves within the public land, for administrative rather than management purposes. The more extensive tracts of publicly owned forest and game reserves are used casually by hunters, hikers, picnickers, and campers. Use of these areas is sharply limited by lack of access and absence of facilities. Controlled, licensed hunting is permitted in Trinidad, and there is a variety of game, including deer, peccary, armadillo, agouti, and a variety of birds shot for sport and meat. Hunting seasons and bag limits are established at the administrative level by the Forest Department.

A limited amount of scientific investigation of the vegetation of Trinidad is being conducted through the University of the West Indies. The flora of the state-owned land, especially, has been well worked over. Most studies of the Trinidadian flora have concentrated on economically important tree species. Dr. John W. Purseglove, of the University, and his students have carried out ecological investigations in the montane forest and at Aripo Savannah. Some attempts are being made to complete collections of the island's fauna, but the project has not proceeded very far. Research on the bats of Trinidad—especially vampire bats and fruit bats—has been done by Dr. Arthur Greenhall, past curator of the National Museum.

The Forest Department has silvicultural research plots scattered throughout the island and also conducts a program of tree breeding and experimental forest plantations.

Pitch Lake is a geological curiosity located in the southern part of Trinidad, about eighteen miles southwest of

San Fernando. The lake covers 114 acres with an uneven surface of hardened pitch. The pitch is mined for use as a base for asphalt, and the lake is also important as the location of numerous archeological finds.

There are no officially designated national historical sites in Trinidad. A number of old mansions on Maraval Road in Port of Spain can be viewed upon request to the owners. Most of the earliest government buildings have been renovated and serve in their original capacities today. The oldest government house, a governor's mansion, is now the National Museum. About four miles east of Port of Spain is Fort George. This small fort, built by the English in the late 1700's, is administered as a part of the forest reserve. The fort is in very poor repair.

VII
Seasonal Forest Islands

The sea breaks white across coral reefs, recovers its brilliant blue in shallow coastal water, then breaks again into white foam against crescents of white sand beach. Beyond spreads a low island, screened with thorny scrub—a seasonal forest island. Apparently, the Arawaks and Caribs found islands such as this inhospitable, for there is little evidence on the seasonal forest islands of important Amerindian settlements. People have not been the direct cause of as much change in the original nature of these islands as they have on the rain forest islands, but their goats have made thorough, long-lasting changes in the vegetation and wildlife. Mangrove swamps appear to be the only natural communities that have escaped the land-denuding work of the goats. All else is picked bare, and much of the soil has eroded away. Although more rain falls than in a true desert, parched barrenness pervades the land as in a desert. Old forts, shipyards, great houses, and commercial buildings reflect the wealth that men accumulated on Antigua and Barbados, where rainfall is abundant enough for successful agriculture. St. Eustatius abounds in relics of its long-vanished leadership in commerce. The other islands show few signs of past or present success in human endeavors.

TABLE 5
SEASONAL FOREST ISLANDS

Islands	Beach and Marine Areas	Inland Natural Areas	Wildlife	Historical and Archeological Sites
Anguilla	Beaches Coral reefs			
Antigua	Beaches Coral reefs			Forts Dockyard buildings Museum Sugar mill
Barbados	Beaches Coral reefs	Forest		
Barbuda	Beaches Coral reefs	Savannas	Frigate birds Guinea fowl Deer Turtles	Estate buildings Fort
St. Barthelemy	Beach			
St. Eustatius		Forests Volcanic crater		Commercial buildings Forts Government buildings Houses Church
St. Martin	Beaches Lagoon			

The scarcity of fresh water imposes ecological and economic limits to productivity, so that neither crops nor tourism can grow freely. The beautiful beaches of Anguilla and Barbuda are almost unused.

Anguilla

Anguilla's most outstanding resources are her coral reefs, which are among the finest in the Caribbean. The reefs at Island Harbor are made of a great variety of corals, though most is very large elkhorn coral *(Acropora palmata)*. Very little rock material is included. The Island Harbor reefs support a large population of spiny lobsters *(Panulirus argus)* which are the raw material of the island's lobster fishing industry.

A second series of reefs of very high quality is located on the south coast, at Forest Bay. The make-up of these reefs is similar to the ones at Island Harbor, with formations of elkhorn coral *(Acropora)* predominating. While the reefs at Forest Bay are less extensive than at Island Harbor, the coral formations have achieved a more spectacular size. Individual branches of elkhorn coral frequently extend beyond twelve feet, with diameters of eighteen to twenty-four inches. For the snorkeler or SCUBA diver, the spectacle of the Forest Bay and Island Harbor reefs is even more impressive than the reefs of Buck Island National Monument, St. Croix, Virgin Islands.

Anguilla's largest beaches are on the south coast, at Rendezvous Bay and Cove Bay. They are made of white sand and are well protected from surf. The outstanding beaches on the north coast are at Road Bay, Crocus Bay, and Island Harbor. Visiting the beaches and swimming are the major forms of outdoor recreation. All of the beaches are publicly owned and easily accessible. The reefs are under public control, though none is officially designated as a park or reserve.

Antigua

Antigua has a larger tourism industry and better air

service than most of the other islands. Beaches, reefs, and the historical area at English Harbor are important attractions.

Antigua is well supplied with excellent, small, white sand beaches, especially along the east and west coasts. The best of these beaches are at Halfmoon Bay in the east, Christian Cove on the southeast coast, and Morris Bay and Ramsey Bay on the west coast. There are also small beaches of good quality at Corbison Point and Fort James on the northwest coast.

All beaches from mean high tide to the water's edge are publicly owned, but except at Fort James the land fronting the beaches mentioned is privately owned. Most beaches of good quality have one or two hotels on them. The undeveloped ones are being held for speculation purposes or with plans for future hotel-building in mind. The local people use the beaches informally for recreation, but the degree to which owners of beach frontage enforce their rights to limit trespass determines the opportunity for the public to use them. The beach at Fort James is a public recreation area.

Most of the coral reef communities off Antigua are along the east and south coasts. They are fringe and patch reefs composed mainly of staghorn and elkhorn coral of the genus *Acropora*. In size and variety of corals, they are reminiscent of the fringe and patch reefs off the American and British Virgin Islands. Antigua's outstanding reefs are near Green Island on the east coast, and at Middle Reef and Cade Reef, off the southwest coast at Goathead.

Admiral Horatio Nelson's Dockyard at English Harbor is one of the most interesting historical sites in the Caribbean. Berkeley Fort was built at the entrance to English Harbor in 1704. Construction of numerous fortifications, docks, and buildings continued through 1787, by which time practically all of the sixteen buildings now standing were completed. Outside the Dockyard area, four small forts guarded the sea and land approaches to the harbor. The largest of these, Fort Monk, was built to defend Falmouth

Harbor, just to the west of the Dockyard area, and to guard against land-based attacks on English Harbor.

The Friends of English Harbor is a quasi-public corporation responsible for the Dockyard area, which is publicly owned. Since 1951, the corporation has solicited funds and supervised work on all of the Dockyard buildings which are to be restored. The reconditioned Admiral's House contains a museum of the history of English Harbor and the Dockyard. Work on several of the smaller buildings is nearly finished, and it proceeds as funds become available. The Friends of English Harbor also plan to restore some of the outlying fortifications. Official records of the number of visitors to Nelson's Dockyard were not available, but the gatekeeper estimated that over 10,000 people per year had visited the area from 1961 through 1963. Visitors pay a small admission fee.

In 1962, the Antigua Archaeological Society, Ltd., was organized to promote the scientific study of Amerindian cultures of Antigua and to assemble an organized collection of artifacts relating to the aboriginal inhabitants of the island.[1]

Barbados

Barbados is the most extensively cultivated island of the Lesser Antilles. Agriculture has been so widespread since the time of European settlement that very little natural vegetation remains. The island has many good beaches for swimming, but few are readily available to the public.

The best beaches for swimming are the small, light brown sand beaches along the southwest, leeward coast between Carlisle Bay and South Point and along the west coast from Paynes Bay to Speightstown. The best beach on the northeast coast, near Bathsheba, is about one-half mile of light brown sand suitable only for surf bathing because it is on the unprotected windward coast. Though beaches from mean high tide to the water are public, most land fronting on the beaches on Barbados is privately owned. The best ones are not easily available to the public because private owners limit access. The government has begun a program of beach and parkland acquisition to provide for more public outdoor recreation opportunity.[2] Two public beaches near Bridgetown provide recreation for local people and tourists. One has a change house and a small restaurant and bar.

Patch and fringe coral reefs are scattered all around the coastline of the island. The best patch reefs are on the windward side where exposure to the open sea makes snorkeling very difficult.

Turner's Hall Wood is a fifty-acre woodland classified by Beard as part evergreen seasonal forest and part semi-evergreen seasonal forest.[3] It is the only relatively undisturbed forest on Barbados. The wood is owned and administered by Turner's Hall Estate, but protected by statute from all forms of exploitation. There are no developments in the Wood to facilitate any form of outdoor recreation other than observation of the fauna and flora. It is used by the public and occasionally by school classes for nature study.

The most interesting natural areas are along the rock-bound coast at the northern end of the island. Due to locally slight rainfall, most of the vegetation is dry evergreen formations. Salt spray blown inland inhibits the growth of the few trees and shrubs scattered across salt-tolerant grass meadows. Cactus and other succulents are common.

Welchman's Hall Gully is a place of botanical interest owned by the Barbados National Trust and open to the public for nature study and recreational outings. The Trust has introduced plants to the area to supplement the existing flora.

Farley Hill, an area of seasonal evergreen forest overlooking the Bathsheba coast, was acquired by the government in 1966 and declared a national park to commemorate the national independence of Barbados. The ruins of the

Farley Hill estate house are included in the new park, but the value of this historic building was greatly reduced by a fire in early 1967.

The one official historical site on Barbados is a restored sugar mill and refinery just north of the city of Bridgetown. It is owned and administered by the Barbados National Trust.

Barbuda

Magnificent beaches, extensive coral reefs, a large mangrove swamp, undisturbed bushy thickets, and natural savannas make Barbuda a center of natural history interest in the Eastern Caribbean. We can think of no other island which offers so fine an opportunity to reserve natural communities of Caribbean seasonal and semi-evergreen plant formations.

The leeward coast beaches of Barbuda are white sand and excellent in quality. The beaches extending from Coco Point northwestward to Spanish Well Point and Palmetto Point are among the finest in the Caribbean. There are other small, high quality beaches farther north, on the leeward side of Cedar Tree Point and Billy Point. All of the beaches are Crown Land, as is the entire island. With the exception of the beach at Coco Point, all are accessible to the public for informal recreation.

The coral reefs that virtually surround Barbuda are perhaps its most outstanding feature. The windward, or eastern, coast reef is almost unbroken from Spanish Point at the southern end of the island to Goat Point at the northern end. Leeward coast reefs of good quality are found from Spanish Well Point to Palmetto Point, with good patch reefs about midway between Palmetto Point and Cedar Tree Point. The reefs at the southern end of the island off Coco Point and in Gravenor Bay are excellent for snorkeling and SCUBA diving. During periods of quiet water, Goat Reef at the northern end of the island is a truly spectacular snorkeling area, surpassing even the reefs off Anguilla.

Patches of open savanna are scattered behind the southeast coast of Barbuda. These open glades of cow grass *(Paspalum bakeri)* are interspersed in dry evergreen brushland. Beard states, "On . . . the island of Barbuda there are savannas which are considered to be 'natural', that is to derive from climatic or edaphic causes. These are the only 'natural' savannas in the Lesser Antilles."[4] However, C. A. Carlozzi found identical, though much smaller, grassland savannas above Forest Bay in Anguilla.

The Billy Point mangrove swamp is a major Leeward Islands nesting site of the frigate bird *(Fregata magnificens)*.

The Barbuda landscape supports populations of two imported animals, Guinea fowl *(Numida melaegris)* and deer *(Odocoileus)*. Both species were stocked on the island several times during the late 1700's by the Codrington family, which owned the island. Both species are well established and range over the entire island.

Local residents and visitors hunt for Guinea fowl, migratory waterfowl, pigeons, and deer. Open seasons for game run for approximately six months of the year beginning in September and ending in March and April, but it is commonly recognized that poaching occurs throughout the closed season. The bag limit on deer is two per person per year. Bag limits on all game birds, including Guinea fowl, ducks, and doves, are ten birds of each kind per day.

The eggs and adults of hawksbill turtles and green turtles are taken during the breeding season. No record of the extent of this harvest is available. Residents of Barbuda claim that the turtle population in the surrounding waters has been declining over the last ten to fifteen years.

There are two sites of historical interest on Barbuda. Highland House is one of several estates built by the Codrington family during the first half of the nineteenth century. It is located in the northwest corner of a low plateau covering the eastern half of the island and known as "The Highlands." Portions of three buildings—the estate house, stables, and servants' quarters—and about seventy yards of aqueduct and a large cistern remain. All of the structures were made from coral and limestone. Disintegration is taking place at a rapid rate.

Martello Tower is a small fort and tower located between Spanish Well Point and Palmetto Point. Its history is not recorded. Residents of Barbuda explain that it was constructed prior to the time of the Codringtons, presumably by buccaneers. The tower could thus have been built at some time from the early 1600's to the early 1700's. It is in such good repair, despite its coral-limestone construction, that we are inclined to place the date very late in that time span.

St. Barthelemy

St. Barthelemy has one very fine beach approximately two miles east of Gustavia, on the southern coast. The beach is about two miles long, composed of light brown sand, and well protected from surf by headlands to the east and west and by being on the leeward coast. It is the island's main outdoor recreation center, but it is used entirely informally and has no facilities. The beach front land is privately owned.

St. Eustatius

An extensive underwater historical area and an unusual volcanic crater make St. Eustatius a very interesting island.

The Quill is the crater of an extinct volcano in the southern end of St. Eustatius. The southeast rim of the crater marks the highest point on the island (1,860 feet), and the floor of the crater is about 500 feet below. The walls of the crater, dropping in most places as sheer cliffs, completely surround the floor. The floor of the crater supports seasonal evergreen forest. Though there is some evidence of second growth forest due to earlier logging, most of the vegetation is relatively undisturbed. The base of the crater's inner wall is covered with dry evergreen forest. A small elfin woodland occupies the high ridge of the crater on the south rim. The outer slopes are also botanically interesting. They support the following plant communities: montane thicket; evergreen bushland; croton-lantana thicket; deciduous seasonal forest; and, where the southern slope nears sea level, strand vegetation and rock pavement vegetation.

Considering that only about two and one-half square miles are involved, the Quill presents a remarkable variety of natural landscapes. Although the Quill is public land, one person uses about one-half acre of the crater floor to grow bananas. This location is not likely to become very popular for agriculture, because the steeper parts of the path going up to the lip of the crater and down into it are inadequate for anything other than foot travel. Little or no recreational use is made of the Quill by the local population, but occasionally visitors to the island make the climb.

St. Eustatius has an unusually large number of interesting historical remnants. During most of the eighteenth century, until 1781 when Britain's Admiral Rodney destroyed the port and town of Oranjestad, St. Eustatius was the most active port of trade in the Lesser Antilles. For a while, it was the richest port in the Americas. Evidence of a prosperous era can be seen in the remains of over twenty fortifications and the submerged ruins of commercial buildings which stretch for more than one-half mile along the beach at Oranjestad. The largest fortifications are Fort Oranje in Oranjestad, Fort Roosevelt on the highest hill north of the town, the fort at Tumble Down Dick on Jenkins Bay, and a fortification at Whitewall on Kay Bay. The government restored Fort Oranje, remounted the old cannon on wooden carriages, and returned them to their original emplacements. The present government buildings are located in the fort, which is maintained with public works funds.

The last preserved sample of "great-house" architecture on St. Eustatius is the town house of Governor de Graff, who held office at the time of the English attack. The house was restored by its current owner with the aid of a Dutch architect and in keeping with the original plans insofar as was possible. Most of the interior wooden parts had to be replaced. Original moldings and door frames were saved in only one room. Brick work on the outside was restored using three hundred year old bricks salvaged from several other ruins in Oranjestad.

Remnants of the governor's country house on the eastern outskirts of Oranjestad are in very bad condition. Masonry work of a Dutch Reformed Church built in 1720 are still standing, but all of the wooden parts, such as the roof and steeple, have collapsed and decayed. The building is owned by the central office of the Dutch Reformed Church in Willemstad, Curacao.

St. Martin

St. Martin has some very fine white sand beaches on the northern, French, coast at Anse des Sables and Grande Case and on the southern, Dutch, coast at Little Bay and Simpson Bay. The beaches are all publicly owned, but the land fronting them is in private ownership. Access to the Little Bay Beach is controlled by a hotel which does not permit use of the beach by the general public.

Simpson Lagoon is an important nursery area for young spiny lobsters *(Panulirus argus)* in the western end of St. Martin. It is a very large lagoon, with an opening to the sea on the Dutch side. A research project begun there by Dr. Ingvar Kristensen aims at increasing lobster production.

VIII
Tropical Desert Islands

The winds that blow across Aruba, Bonaire, and Curacao have just lost most of their moisture over South America, so the islands are drenched with sun but not with water. Green beach plants sparsely fringe the brown, salt-flecked interior land where cactus and thorn forest prevail.

Curiously, men have valued these desert isles from the time of aboriginal settlement to the present. The islands are rich in archeological proof that Amerindians occupied the land. The Dutch found salt and an ideal location for commerce along the sea routes to South American ports. Now, huge oil refineries generate wealth uncommon in the Caribbean islands. Also unlike the rest of the Caribbean, the social organization of the desert islands has been urban from the beginning of European settlement. The great houses of other centuries are in the cities, not the countryside.

Ingenuity and money have overcome the natural shortage of fresh water. Today, water from the sea is distilled, but years ago wells provided what was needed. Old wind-driven water pumps dot the islands, recalling earlier efforts to extract the underground supplies, now exhausted.

TABLE 6

TROPICAL DESERT ISLANDS

Islands	Beach and Marine Areas	Inland Natural Areas	Wildlife	Historical and Archeological Sites
Aruba	Beach Coral reefs	Diorite boulders		Petrographs and petroglyphs
Bonaire		Plant communities	Flamingoes Parrots	Plantation buildings Navigational pylons
Curacao	Beaches Coral reefs		Green turtles	Petrographs and petroglyphs Fort Houses

Aruba

Palm Beach is a three-mile-long white sand beach on the west coast of Aruba. It is Aruba's main swimming center and one of the finest of Caribbean beaches. In recent years, the government has increased the recreational value of Palm Beach by constructing a shoreline highway along most of the beach and installing picnic tables shaded by palm thatched canopies. Public works funds financed the project.

Patch coral communities are scattered along the western shore of Aruba between Manchebo and Kudarebe. The reefs are built mostly by corals of the genus *Acropora,* with *A. cervicornis* appearing most often.

Very large diorite boulders are strewn across several areas of the northeast coast near the town of Fontein. In many instances, the boulders are piled atop one another, making small "boulder hills." The compacted diorite quartz sand of which the boulders are made is highly erodable, and years of weathering have produced many unusual shapes. All of the diorite boulder areas are privately owned. The Aruba Tourist Board provided a parking lot at one of them, and a small area around a major pile of boulders has been landscaped. Signs mounted on various boulders give names to the imaginary figures that resulted from the erosion process. Local people and tourists go there for family outings and picnics.

Aruba has a wealth of petrographs and petroglyphs in several locations scattered about the island. In many instances, petrographs were rendered on massive diorite boulders. The most famous of the rock paintings are in a cave known as Quadirikiri, on the northeast coast about one mile from Fontein. The seven petrograph and petroglyph areas viewed by the senior author were privately owned but open to the public. We do not know the status of the other sites.

The Netherlands Antilles National Parks Foundation has shown some interest in establishing several of the areas as archeological sites. However, neither the Parks Foundation nor the Aruba government has taken any official action yet to protect these places.

Bonaire

Bonaire is known as the "flamingo island." It is the southernmost of three nesting areas of the Caribbean flamingo *(Phoenicopterus ruber)*. The other two areas are on the Yucatán Peninsula and on the island of Inagua in the Bahamas. Pekelmeer, a brine lake in the southern end of Bonaire, and lands bordering Pekelmeer on the southeast comprise an important feeding area and the major nesting area for the southern flock. Flamingoes also feed at Gotomeer, another brine lake in the low hills of northern Bonaire. Dr. Ingvar Kristensen, of the Caribbean Marine Biological Institute in Curacao, reports that flamingoes nest on the mud flats north of Gotomeer occasionally, but the amount of nesting there is slight compared to the major nesting areas in the south of the island. Interest in the flamingoes' food supply led Dr. Kristensen to study the invertebrates of Pekelmeer and Gotomeer.

Northwest of Gotomeer is a small brine lake called Slagbaai which provides food for the flamingoes. The Slagbaai region is also the territory of the Bonaire parrot *(Amazona barbadensis rothschildii)*, a species indigenous to Bonaire.

In addition to the preservation of birdlife, the three areas mentioned above could provide protection for four kinds of plant communities—salt flat vegetation, strand vegetation, Croton-Lantana thicket, and thorny woodland— if they were made nature reserves.

There are no officially designated parks or reserves on Bonaire. Laws dealing with protection of the flamingoes and other wildlife of the island are administered from the Lieutenant Governor's office through the Bonaire Police Department. A law was passed in 1957 restricting use of the air space over the entire island except for the approach path to the airport. The law was a consequence of a low-level aerial observation of the flamingo nesting and feeding grounds at Pekelmeer the previous year which resulted in the birds leaving the island entirely for a few years.

The Bonaire parrot is subject to harvest by residents of Bonaire who collect young birds for sale as pets in the Curacao market. Dr. Kristensen believes that depredations made upon the nests in this manner over the past decade have reduced the range of the birds, which once covered the entire northern half of the island, to its present location on the Slagbaai estate. Laws protecting these birds are poorly enforced. Slagbaai remains a sanctuary because it is in private ownership and trespass is not allowed by the owner.[1]

All of the Pekelmeer area is in public ownership, as is part of the Gotomeer shoreline. The Netherlands Antilles National Parks Foundation wishes to establish national parks at the three major nesting and feeding grounds of the flamingoes and parrots. Watching the birds is a major recreational activity of the island's people and tourists.

On the narrow strip of land between the west shore of Pekelmeer and the sea are the remains of a plantation house, slave quarters, and two navigational pylons built in the 1670's. At this estate, salt was produced from the brine of Pekelmeer. Because of the extremely dry climate on Bonaire, the masonry structures have weathered well and are mostly intact. They receive a small amount of maintenance through public works funds.

The recreational and scenic value of the northern part of the island is being increased by the construction of a paved seacoast highway running north from Kralendijk, along the shoreline of Gotomeer, and inland to the small town of Rincon. The value of the coastline portion of the highway is enhanced by several turnouts for parking cars and a hiking path, parallel to the highway, which enables people to walk along the coastline and onto the small bays and beaches between the numerous headlands.

Curacao

Most of Curacao's beaches are small and, except near West Point, made of sand mixed with coarse gravel or cobble-sized stones. The West Point beaches have fine, white sand, but they are not heavily used because they are too far from the Willemstad area, and public transportation is not available.

The patch and fringe reefs scattered along the southwest coast of Curacao are made of a variety of corals. The most prevalent corals in the patch reefs are of the genus *Acropora*, especially *A. cervicornis*. However, dominance varies from place to place. Other well represented genera are *Porites*, finger coral; *Meandrina* and *Colpophyllia*, brain corals; and *Millepora*, stinging coral. Fringe reefs are mostly dominated by elkhorn coral *(A. palmata)*.

An important breeding site for green turtles *(Chelonia mydas)* and hawksbill turtles *(Eretmochelys imbricata)* is at Klein Curacao, a small coral island midway between Curacao and Bonaire. The island is a publicly owned dependency of Curacao. Turtles and their eggs are taken in large numbers by local people and transient fishermen. There are no laws protecting turtles or their eggs at present, but they are contemplated for such time in the future when the need seems more obvious.[2]

Like Aruba, Curacao is rich in aboriginal cultural remains, especially petrographs and petroglyphs. Unlike Aruba, where most of the sites are in the interior of the island, all of Curacao's are along the northeast and southwest coasts. The greatest concentration of petroglyphs in Curacao is in the Hato region at about the center of the northeast coast. They generally appear along the back walls and ceilings of undercuts in a long cliff which was the result of wave action at a higher sea level. Petrographs are also found near Santa Martha on the southwest coast. All of the petrograph and petroglyph sites are in private ownership. The Netherlands Antilles National Parks Foundation is interested in acquiring them for establishment as island historical sites.

Fort Amsterdam occupies the southeast point of land at the entrance to the harbor at Willemstad. The outer walls of the fort have been completely restored, but the inside has been considerably modified, due primarily to a hotel which was built inside the fort. Many of the quarters and the old warehouses which were part of the walls of the fort are now occupied by stores and offices. The main quadrangle was originally built to house the major government offices and is still used for that purpose. Many of the government offices in Fort Amsterdam are going to be completely rebuilt or replaced, but the plans call for duplicating the old style and construction in the new buildings.

The Parks Foundation owns and maintains five estate houses dating from the late 1700's that serve as historical sites and as guest houses for visitors to the government of the Netherlands Antilles. The houses were restored and furnished in a style appropriate to their age.

PART THREE

Proposals for Development

CARIBBEAN FLAMINGOS AT SLAGBAAI, BONAIRE

IX
Planning for Conservation and Economic Development

Any accounting of measures taken to preserve and develop the resources inventoried in the preceding section makes a dismal picture. Only a small number of these assets have received some measure of attention, and this attention varies greatly, from the elaborate efforts of the Friends of English Harbor on behalf of restoring Nelson's Dockyard in Antigua to the simple placement of a plaque on a crumbling building. Most often, it has been the more impressive remains of European settlement that have been conserved, as opposed to the wealth of natural beauty. In only a few cases are there effective provisions for keeping worthwhile natural areas in their present condition.

The intrinsic value of the islands' important natural and historical sites seems reason enough to protect and care for such areas, but in view of the economic difficulties which beset the islands, it is not surprising that conservation efforts lag behind the struggle to provide jobs, improved education, health care, and other human needs. We believe, however, that conservation and development of natural and historical resources could contribute to the economic development of the islands. This belief is based on the theory that, for most Eastern Caribbean islands, tourism expansion is the most promising means to economic progress, and that the region's natural and historical sites can help sustain the tourism industry. Well-laid plans for the use of these sites and for the whole environment should result not only in a strong basis for tourism, but also in a more pleasing environment for the people of the islands and retention of the singular characteristics of each island.

Though public interest seldom turns to the protection of the natural environment and historic remains, it is always attuned to economic well-being. In this sphere, public pressure is the greatest and political leaders' attention the sharpest. Economic planners in the several governments of the islands are primarily concerned with finding the means to develop the island economies in new ways or to revitalize existing ones. Political leaders are most sensitive to the need for new and expanded employment opportunities for the ever-growing labor force, and for increasing the extent of island exports.

Thus it would seem that the most effective case for conservation and development of the islands' bountiful resources would be the demonstration that this course also leads to economic benefits.

A further look at the region's economic problems should clarify the importance of tourism. The relationship between tourism and natural and historic sites is considered next, followed by some thoughts on physical planning and its effects on the quality of island living, national identity, and economic progress.

Tourism and economic vitality

Except for Trinidad, Aruba, and Curacao, it can generally be said that the Eastern Caribbean islands suffer from too much of a sameness in their economic condition. Basically, the islands depend upon agriculture and tourism. The larger islands have, in the main, relatively rich soil resources and a climate favorable for cultivation. To varying degrees, all of the islands contain natural and historical features and a climate attractive to tourists seeking tropical vacations. But in agriculture, as in tourism, the islands are competitive rather than complementary to one another. Sugar, bananas, cocoa, and cotton dominate the agricultural scene. All of these commodities are subject to world market and price conditions, the vagaries of which are well known. In addition, there are many other areas of the world producing identical agricultural products, generally on a much larger, more efficient scale than in the West Indies.

The dominance of cash crops for export has forced the islands to become mercantile to a fault, so that none enjoys a favorable balance of trade. All of the islands import most of their foodstuff. Diversification of agricultural production to supply domestic food requirements would obviously reduce the drain on the island's meager supply of hard currency available for international trade. Standing in the way are such difficulties as lack of specialized agricultural and merchandising skills and the absence of the necessary marketing apparatus.[1]

Sea transport is fundamental to the economic wellbeing of the people. Food, clothing, manufactured goods, and raw materials for industry are sent to the islands by sea. Exports also depend upon ships. Surprisingly, few of the islands are able to provide adequate sea transport facilities such as docks, wharfs, and warehouses. Of the twenty-two islands studied here, only Curacao, Trinidad, Barbados, and St. Vincent have deep water harbors. On all the other islands, passengers and materials are loaded and unloaded by lighters.

All of the islands have airfields, but the air service to them varies greatly. There is a commonly expressed belief in the islands that tourism is heavily dependent on plentiful and frequent air service. It is true that islands with strong tourism industries also have very good air service. Antigua, Aruba, Barbados, Curacao, Guadeloupe, Martinique, and Trinidad receive international flights daily. Other islands accept smaller planes of feeder lines. Night-flying facilities, which are increasingly important, are presently not available in Anguilla, Dominica, Grenada, Montserrat, Saba, St. Barthelemy, St. Eustatius, St. Lucia, and St. Vincent. Air service to the smaller islands—Barbuda, Saba, St. Barthelemy, and St. Eustatius—is severely limited as to both frequency and size of plane.

Air freight has been increasing at the rate of 20 to 25 per cent annually over the last several years through large ports such as Barbados and Antigua. A shortage of return cargo contributes to the persistence of high rates.[2]

The dependence upon overseas markets, especially markets in the relevant colonial countries, has throughout the history of the region focused the concern and dependence of the island peoples on Europe, and in more recent times the United States. This has resulted in the failure of the islands to become linked economically with one another. Deficiencies in marketing system, trade agreements, and inter-island shipping inhibit trade which might otherwise develop.[3]

If one spends any time at all in the Caribbean, it is impossible to avoid hearing opinions on the economic conditions of the islands from people in all segments of society. These expressions are summed up in the belief that the Caribbean islands must somehow become more firmly linked together in the political and economic spheres if their major problems in economic advancement are ever to be solved. The free trade area established by Guyana, Antigua, and Barbados is a recent step in this direction. Yet the traditional means for international co-operation at the economic level are easily thwarted by the competitiveness of the island economies and the long period of economic insularity that stand as major obstacles to any form of meaningful economic integration.

The most recent assessment of possibilities for economic improvement in the Eastern Caribbean is in the *Report of the Tri-Partite Economic Survey of the Eastern Caribbean*,[4] conducted from January to April, 1966, by the governments of Great Britain, Canada, and the United States. The survey covered Barbados and the islands of the seven unfederated government units of the British West Indies, of which nearly all are now Associated States. It evaluated economic and social factors currently impeding development of the islands and suggested steps necessary to their becoming economically viable. In this report, viability was defined as the elimination of the need for grants-in-aid and non-commercial loans as a regular fixture of the public economy. Recommendations for achieving viability aimed at increasing the islands' exports at a faster rate than imports.

While the survey team saw possibilities of improvement in industry, agriculture, and commerce, these were anticipated largely within the internalized portions of the economy rather than in the externalized portions which provide avenues for exports.

Tourism, as an earner of overseas money, was believed to hold the greatest promise for future expansion of exports. It was in this realm that the islands appear to have a natural advantage for supplying a market which at present is growing and, in all probability, will continue to grow.

The 1963 *Annual Report* of the Caribbean Organization corroborates this view:

> The importance of the tourist industry in the Caribbean area can hardly be overemphasized. The vast majority of the countries possess no mineral wealth, but all are blessed with the natural requirements, some more profusely than others, upon which a tourist industry thrives most readily.[5]

An estimated 1,400,000 visitors reached the Caribbean islands in 1962. Income accruing to these islands was approximately $200,000,000—about 7 per cent of the total national income of the region.[6]

For islands which do not have large industries, as Curacao does, or a variety of industrial, commercial, and agricultural enterprises, as Trinidad does, tourism contributes a much higher proportion of total national income. For Antigua, in 1962, tourism revenue equaled 168 per cent of the value of visible exports. For Barbados, tourism revenue equaled 32 per cent of the value of visible exports.[7]

Tourism revenue has contributed favorably to the economic and social advancement of many of the islands. The multiplier effect of tourism dollars is felt through primary, secondary, and tertiary level service industries which surround the major resort and hotel enterprises, and, with a few exceptions, returns to capital and labor are favorable.

A striking characteristic of the existing Caribbean tourism industry, its spotty distribution among the islands, is demonstrated by the following statistics from the Caribbean Organization:

> There is a concentration of visitors and visitor expenditure in three or four centres in the area. Puerto Rico, for example, realized some 30.8% of the total estimated expenditure of tourists who visited the Caribbean area in 1961, while Jamaica received 25.7%, the U. S. Virgin Islands 14.7%, and Trinidad and Tobago 11.4%. This makes a total of 82.6% of Caribbean tourism revenue accruing to four countries. The remaining 17.4% is shared by 15 other countries of the area.[8]

The tourism industry is also seasonal, so that employment and income are concentrated in the winter months, from November to April. Consequently, the 1966 *Economic Survey* recommended programs for future development of the industry to provide a more diversified, year-around source of income and to assist in distributing tourism revenues to a wider assortment of islands. Not only are individual island programs needed, but also an image of regional diversity and regional tourism.

The co-operative advertising program of the Caribbean

Tourist Association gives some hope that regionalization of some aspects of the tourism industry can be accomplished despite competition among the several islands in attracting their respective shares of tourism revenues.

The fact remains that tourism, despite its uneven distribution and seasonality, offers the most realistic hope of economic advancement for most Eastern Caribbean islands.

Conservation and tourism

It is our argument that the goal of conserving unique natural and historical resources of the Caribbean might be reached by clearly demonstrating the relevance of these resources to the successful exploitation of tourism in the Caribbean, which means to the economic self-interest of island people and governments.

A market analysis showing a tidy dollars-and-cents relationship between investment in parks and historical sites and the tourism industry would certainly aid the island governments in evaluating plans for such investment, but clear-cut analyses of this kind are not available. Nevertheless, several facts and conditions lead us to conclude that the relationship is indeed operative.

The governments of the Caribbean were aware of the islands' potential for supporting a strong tourism industry in the early 1940's. The Anglo-American Caribbean Commission undertook in 1943 "to carry out a preliminary survey for the purpose of bringing within a single comprehensive report a description of the attractions, existing and potential, which the Caribbean has to offer tourists."[9] The report of Mr. Coert DuBois, U. S. Commissioner to the Commission, covered all of the Caribbean islands, summarizing their existing facilities and potentials for development. The report included a survey of beaches and scenic sites, these being obviously among the assets recognized as worthy of attention. Thus it seems that the earliest organized effort to develop Caribbean tourism recognized the natural attractions of the region as well as its climate and its accessibility for the American market.

On the islands that have successful tourism industries, —Trinidad and Tobago, Antigua, Barbados, Aruba, and Curacao—the more obvious assets such as climate and beaches are the primary tourist attractions, rather than unique natural or historic sites. However, on both Antigua and Trinidad and Tobago, historic sites and natural areas are featured prominently in the tourist literature circulated by the island tourist boards and the commercial concerns which exist on tourism—hotels, airlines, and steamship companies. This suggests that unique sites are at least useful in supplementing the more obvious attractions of the islands—a usefulness which the Anglo American Caribbean Commission apparently recognized, also.

A direct, causative connection is more difficult to establish, but the experiences of Puerto Rico and St. John, of the United States Virgin Islands, are instructive. Both are highly successful tourism centers, and both exhibit a relative abundance of developed historic and natural attractions. But did the development of unique sites aid tourism, or vice versa?

At least one authority concluded that a thriving tourism industry leads naturally to the establishment of natural areas and historic sites. In a paper presented at a Caribbean-wide seminar on planning methods, Miguel A. Barasorda, Director of the Facilities Development Division, Department of Tourism of Puerto Rico, states:

> The fact remains that well-guided tourism brings about improvements in living conditions, preservation, and interpretation of historic monuments, conservation of sites of outstanding natural beauty; development of music festivals, expositions of plastic arts, development of handicraft, improvement of architecture, as well as the architecture of the environment which gives form to the cities. Therefore, tourism can be made to preserve rather than disfigure the cultural as well as the physical character of the country.[10]

The truth of Mr. Barasorda's statement is visible in Puerto Rico today, but benefits have also flowed in the opposite direction. The development of some major historic sites and natural areas preceded the blossoming of the Puerto Rican tourism trade by several years, rather than ensuing from it. The establishment of the national historic sites in San Juan, El Morro and Fort San Cristobal, and the rain forest park at El Yunque were stimulated more by precedents established in the United States than in response to popular interest in Puerto Rico. The historic sites were established in 1949 and are administered by the United States National Park Service. The initial steps to open the rain forest on El Yunque for recreation were taken by the United States Forest Service. Obviously, these places were not the sole cause, nor even a major cause of Puerto Rico's tourism industry, but it seems fair to say that they contribute to its success.

The experience of St. John argues more clearly for the development of natural resources as a stimulus to economic expansion. The island has developed a tourism industry around its scenery, history, and natural resources. Approximately three-quarters of St. John is circumscribed by the boundaries of a United States National Park which served as the basis upon which to build a tourism economy.

St. John's resources are distinctly limited. It has poor soil, no commercial forests, little water, and no important minerals. However, compensating for these deficiencies are numerous sites of historical interest, appealing scenery, and many excellent white sand beaches. Moreover, tourism seemed to island leaders to be the primary possibility for creating an internally generated economy.

Prior to the national park development, St. John most resembled in economic condition the Caribbean islands of the sixth economic type described in Chapter III—islands characterized by subsistence agriculture and government grants-in-aid. As in those islands, there was very little internally generated economic activity. Public works and money received from islanders working away from home constituted the major sources of income for the people.

Since the park opened in 1956, the economy of St. John has expanded rapidly. Employment opportunities with the Park Service and a major hotel have largely absorbed the previous surplus labor force. Allied services such as restaurants, gift shops, car rentals, taxi guides, and guided tours have resulted.[11]

St. John is successful largely because its scenery is consolidated into a single public holding administered by an experienced agency, and because sufficient capital was available for the construction of a first-class resort facility that is in itself an attraction to tourists.

Another example of economic expansion following park development happened in Teton County, Wyoming. The establishment of Jackson Hole National Monument, in Teton County, was finally settled in 1950. Since then, a major hotel, motels, and a variety of other tourist-oriented businesses have opened or expanded. The number of tourists in the county and the county's economy have increased sharply. The increase is partly a reflection of trends general to the state of Wyoming and the entire United States. But the rate of economic expansion has been higher for Teton County than for the whole state or the whole country.[12]

Park development alone did not produce successful tourism industries in the cases mentioned. Other indispensable elements included capital for hotel building, skilled management and work force, adequate transportation to and within the area, availability of utilities, and publicity. But at Jackson Hole and St. John, the developed parks were fundamental to the entire undertaking. This function of parks is worth serious consideration in the land-use and economic planning process, particularly in the Eastern Caribbean where there seldom is either land or money to spare.

At first glance, the Caribbean islands with economies based on subsistence agriculture and grants-in-aid, as St. John was, seem to offer the most hopeful opportunity for tying conservation to tourism development. Because natural and historical areas constitute nearly the whole resource base, their development is clearly in the economic interest of the islands. However, these islands are impoverished. Unless they are able to acquire sufficient capital for the other elements of a tourism industry, the precedent of St. John will remain beyond their reach.

The impoverished islands' natural areas benefit from a kind of preservation by default which is symptomatic of economic stagnation, for no significant enterprises impinge upon the areas. The historical sites remain vulnerable to weathering and vandalism. In contrast to this state is that of the large group of islands in the third economic category, consisting of dominantly agricultural islands. These latter islands, characterized by rapidly growing populations and struggling economies, offer no such *laissez-faire* protection to their natural areas.

However, in the case of the agricultural islands, there is considerable potential for tourism-oriented development of natural and historic sites. All of the economic and social needs are intensely felt on these islands. Government leaders, economic planners, and private individuals are eager to make presently unused resources fill a productive role in the islands. The agricultural islands are actively searching for resources to which investment capital can be applied. While the possibility of action exists, therefore, such activity can also mean that alternate uses may be proposed and effected for sites that should be preserved for unique natural or historical quality.

Extensive logging in the forests of Dominica and proposals to use St. Lucia's Morne Fortune for house lots are examples that readily come to mind. In both cases, political and community leaders have shown an appreciation, common to all of the islands, of the long-range social benefits that derive from maintaining intact their natural and cultural inheritance.

No matter how profound it may be, though, appreciation fills no wallets. Consequently, island leaders are pressed by their constituents to take advantage of any opportunity to increase employment and income. An alliance of conservation and tourism could work toward both ends.

Environmental planning

Whatever hopes for future economic growth in the Caribbean islands may rest upon tourism, we believe attention must be paid to the resource base contributing to the tourism-recreational environment as well as to capital and labor. It is in the resources, both natural and historic, that the elements of diversity are found which characterize the small islands of the Eastern Caribbean and provide a truly rewarding vacation experience for mainland as well as inter-island tourists.

Throughout the Caribbean, a common anxiety arose in our discussions with people concerned both about problems of economic development and about preservation of natural and historic resources. It is the often-stated fear that too active an encouragement of the tourism industry will release upon the islands the most undesirable forms of unbridled commercialism. Underlying this idea is the belief that the islands have a unique character emanating from the combined influences of climate, natural features, and human activity. Their character may be grossly distorted by rampant tourism. Sufficient experience has been accumulated on several of the islands to warrant some expressions of caution about the less desirable forms of commercial enterprise that can and have accompanied tourism development. That this is a present and future danger is admitted. That this potential danger will in fact be manifested if tourism is introduced or increased on the islands is not necessarily so. Clearly there is opportunity for planning and social control over the way in which the landscape is used and developed. Badly placed or undesirable forms of commercial enterprise can be prevented from taking hold and detracting esthetically or economically from the overall potential for desirable tourism development.

The islands of the Eastern Caribbean are particularly susceptible to the deteriorating effects of unplanned physical development simply because they are small and their resources are very limited. With tourism destined to play a significant role in the economic life of the islands, full consideration should also be given to the reciprocal influences which the other major aspects of island life—agriculture, industry, commerce, and the public infrastructure—have upon each other and upon tourism.

It would seem then that a major input in physical planning and landscape design must be added to the efforts being made in economic and social planning for the development of tourism and all other primary sectors of the island economy. This type of planning, as in economic and social planning, has a strong time element and is in fact a continuing process. It is less concerned with specific layout and design of individual components of the landscape, and more concerned with the overall arrangement of those components within a regional or island-wide context.

Economic development planning can be carried out with minimal attention to the overall environment and especially to that part of the environment having to do with landscape quality and esthetic character. This has happened in the United States and is all too evident today in nations that are caught up in the activities of promoting industrialization and commercialization to the exclusion of concerns for the total environment quality. Leaders in the governments of the Caribbean islands should be especially aware of the effects of successful short run economic development on the general long run physical character of the islands.

Most economic enterprises are concerned only with the functional quality of their immediate location. The visual quality of the general surroundings is not usually a vital concern. The tourism industry, which relies on a high-quality total environment, must take into consideration not only immediate sites occupied by tourism enterprises, but also the entire landscape from background to foreground. The many elements of island life become part of and influence the environment in which tourism or holiday activities take place. To the tourist, agriculture, industry, commercial development, roads, public buildings, open spaces, mountains and forests, shoreline and sea are all part of the landscape mix wherein he may find a pleasurable holiday atmosphere or a chaotic and unsatisfying milieu.

To accomplish the type of physical planning called for requires for the most part an orientation in planning concepts not often found. Economic and social welfare planning has been a feature of island government activity for some time now, but physical planning, especially in the total environment sense, is rarely undertaken by even some of the most advanced and wealthy urban-industrialized nations.

Where such planning has been carried out, it is increasingly evident that not only the services of professionally trained physical planners are required, but also a wider participation in the planning process by all of the major segments of government and private agencies. Governments choosing to embark on this type of planning exercise should be prepared for the reluctance of economic planners to participate. This seems to be especially true in countries where economic development planning has held sway over the decision makers in the past. It is true that many elements of the total environment planning goals and activities will not lend themselves easily to economic analysis. This is because there is a very long time period implied in environmental planning, and economic tools for assessing probable financial returns or social benefits are as yet insufficiently developed.

We contend, however, that total environment planning, though not entirely economic in its procedures, is valuable and needed if there is to be, even for the short run, a rational approach to economic development and the expansion and improvement of the infrastructure.

Some readjustment of the priority given to different economic and social elements is called for. On most islands, tourism appears to hold the strongest long-run potential for economic growth, yet in most cases island governments have been willing to sacrifice environmental quality for the sake of maximum efficiency in industrial enterprises or enlarging the infrastructure.

Bonaire illustrates this conflict of values. In May, 1964, the Bonaire island government concluded arrangements with a North American salt company for the construction of an extensive area of salt pans. Employment from the salt industry is expected to provide full-time employment for about sixty workers. The salt industry should bring a significant gain to the economy of the island, but there is a considerable risk to tourism involved. The salt pans will occupy some of the nesting area of the island's major tourist attraction—the large flamingo colony. A compromise has been worked out wherein the more active and noisy aspects of the salt operation will be kept as far from the nesting area as possible. Thus, a natural resource receives protection at the expense of some efficiency for an industry.

From the point of view of our study, it is obvious that the natural and historic resources of unique scenic, scientific, or historical value should comprise a major element in the overall landscape that supports and enhances the present and future tourism industries as they may develop. It is appropriate to include some resources, such as beaches, as integral parts of tourist or public recreation facilities. Most resources, however, are less appropriate to this assignment, and we believe their value lies in their supporting role as points of special interest within the overall landscape of the islands.

While regional planning and design carried on within the broad framework discussed above places new demands upon all levels of public decision making, it should not be thought of as applying solely to the creation of a pleasant experience for tourists. Any statement of planning goals or desirable environmental attributes that stems from a wish simply to please tourists risks evoking the least common denominator of environmental quality and possibly contributing to uniformity of landscape throughout the Eastern Caribbean region.

The natural and historical qualities which create the unique character of the individual islands are also of concern to the island people themselves.

The very possibility that the islands may succeed in improving their economic and social conditions justifies re-evaluation of land use priorities. Accelerating popular interest in all forms of leisure and outdoor recreation is a mark of societies that are becoming more urban, industrial, and commercial. Trinidad is already well into this process. Public pressure there is sufficient to have stimulated an active program by the government to include national parks and equivalent reserves and outdoor recreation areas in the overall scheme for the national land use plan. The Trinidad plan recommends development of a system of high density recreation areas, general outdoor recreation areas, unique natural areas, scenic areas, and historical sites.[13]

A prudent course for people confident in their own future would be to make sure in advance that recreation lands suitable for a variety of activities will be available.

It seems to us that the physical planning process should begin with identification of national characteristics in the landscape and environment. Here is the logical starting place for establishing intentions and goals for what an island landscape really should be. Here, surely, is something of concern to the island people.

A planning process that begins with the natural attributes and cultural applications of an island ensures that the particular characteristics of the island are fundamental to physical planning goals and development guidelines.

It is precisely to these ends that we urge full attention be given to the natural and historical assets which each island contains in some degree and which separates it in character from its neighboring islands and countries. The long run benefits from this approach to environmental planning and design are: first, a more pleasing and satisfying environment for the people of the islands that can stimulate pride in national character as it is manifested in the landscape; and second, an environmental base which attracts and supports continuing growth of a tourism industry capable of giving the visitor a real sense of diversity throughout the region as well as imparting to him an acquaintance with the profound historic and natural links between the individual islands.

X

Institutional, Technical, and Financial Needs

Once natural and historic areas are incorporated into a basic land use plan, their functional role in the total environment is protected. But to be fully useful, either for local recreation or tourism, the areas need to be developed to an appropriate extent. Although island governments may recognize the need, they have not often involved themselves in protecting and developing these areas. This failure can be laid to the lack of two resources, capital and "know-how." Wise assistance to the islands can make the financial burden lighter and provide the necessary technical and institutional means for accomplishing a valuable program.

Financial assistance

In the islands studied, total government expenditures exceed total tax receipts by two to five times. The difference is usually made up by grants from the metropolitan countries. It is also typical that recurrent government expenditures of these islands consume around 80 per cent of the total annual budget.[1] This leaves a very small amount for new capital expenditure, most of which must be directed toward expanding and improving presently inadequate public services such as roads, power, schools, hospitals, and internal communications.

Governments on these islands may recognize the cultural and economic value of unique natural areas and historic sites. They may be willing to forego alternate uses for these sites in order to keep them intact. They may recognize the economic justification for investing government capital in their development and improvement. But without financial assistance from sources outside the islands, they are not likely to be able to carry through any such program.

Generally, the islands need two forms of financial assistance, in land acquisition and in site development.

Land acquisition

On most of the study islands, financial assistance in land acquisition could be held to a minimum. As may be seen in the inventory, most relevant sites are currently in public hands, especially in the case of natural areas and scenic sites. Though fortresses and other historic government buildings are typically on public land, other sites of historical interest such as estate houses, commercial buildings, and relics of pre-Columbian history are in private ownership.

On many of the islands, land fronting beaches is privately held. Most of the islands do not feel public pressure for the establishment of outdoor recreation areas on the beaches because private beach development is sparse enough that beaches are still open to public access and use. However, where tourism industries are expanding, beach frontage is taken over by hotels and resorts which deny access to the general public. Antigua and Barbados are two examples of this situation. If other islands experience significant growth in resort facilities, it is likely that they too will see a reduction in the number of high-quality beaches available for public use. Therefore, land acquisition for preserving public access to beaches should also be carried out.

Financial resources from outside the islands could play an important role in helping the island governments to acquire lands in all categories.

Site development

Financial aid for site development is needed for a wide range of projects, from restoration and stabilization of historic sites to construction of access roads to parks and equivalent areas.

In some instances, assistance could be given for projects of this kind on a cost-sharing basis. The Barbados government has shared costs on a fifty-fifty basis with the Barbados National Trust to develop Welchman's Hall Gully and to restore the sugar mill historic site.

When land for parks and reserves has been acquired, governments could contribute to development by diverting a portion of their public works capability to the development of national parks and historic sites. On Bonaire, the construction of a scenic highway, turnouts, footpaths, and picnic areas along the northwest coast was accomplished through a public works project which was partly intended to provide employment.

Gifts from private individuals provide another means for cost-sharing. On Montserrat, one landowner was willing to give a substantial amount of acreage to the government for a national park if the government or another donor would provide the funds necessary for physical development. A variation of this theme can be found in Martinique, where the Natural History Society believed it would receive a donation from private owners of land to be established as a nature preserve if the Society could guarantee the required maintenance and protection.[2]

Technical and institutional problems

An outcome of the lack of conservation activity has been the failure to build up institutions and bodies of technical personnel that could adequately plan, develop, and administer conservation programs. Even in Trinidad and Tobago, where strong efforts are being made toward preservation and development, there is no single agency or institution responsible for the program. Responsibility is divided among several divisions of several ministries, each setting its own policy.

Among the other islands in the study group that have quasi-governmental corporate groups, at least a portion of the problem is taken care of. However, the trusts and foundations of the Netherlands Antilles, Antigua, Grenada, Martinique, St. Kitts, St. Lucia, and Barbados are made up chiefly of interested citizens who have no particular professional expertise in nature preservation, historic site development, or public outdoor recreation. Depending upon the quantity and quality of their overseas affiliations, such groups have primarily functioned as money-raising agencies. The most successful group has been the Friends of English Harbor on Antigua, whose efforts have been rigidly confined to the restoration of a single historical site, Nelson's Dockyard.

The Barbados National Trust, the Friends of Morne Fortune Association of St. Lucia, the Grenada National Trust, and the Netherlands Antilles National Parks Foundation are set up to act across the broad front of nature preservation and development of historical sites, though their activities to date have been mostly confined to historic buildings.

Despite the fact that the incorporated trusts and foundations do not always achieve their full potentials, there is no question that they have made a significant contribution to their respective islands. Given the present attitudes and financial limitations of the people and governments, the few accomplishments to date would not otherwise have been achieved. In view of these experiences, the formation of similar groups in the other islands and countries would be advisable as a first step toward making the efforts of the interested persons of each island more effective.

Conservation trusts or foundations

A trust or foundation should be concerned with all phases of nature preservation, historic sites, and places of archeological interest, for the following reasons:

First, the islands are small, and one trust or foundation could serve an entire island without being forced to deal with a geographical area too large for efficient administration.

Second, most of the islands have but a few outstanding natural areas or historical sites. Thus, a single organization would not have the problem of dealing with a multiplicity of sites.

Third, it was the authors' experience that the people who are interested in nature preservation are also interested in archeology and history. These are few in number on each island and could be incorporated into a single organization able to treat with the full range of the members' interests.

Island trusts or foundations could serve in the following ways:

a. They could follow the acceptable precedent already established in the study islands and other countries of soliciting gifts of money and property from both private and public sources inside and outside the island.

b. They could assume responsibility for development and administration of parks and equivalent reserves without removing them from the general sphere of public control. When governments do wish to express an interest directly or if they acquire financial resources that could be applied to protection or development, they could participate by granting money or providing government services without incurring the expense of administration or establishing new government offices.

c. Island trusts or foundations would be able to make

contact with similar groups in the metropolitan countries and affiliate with them. Such affiliation took place between the Barbados National Trust and the British National Trust, and between the Martinique History Society and the French National Museum. Affiliations of this sort by foundations and trusts on the islands would be a means of attaching their interests and concerns to the metropolitan organizations. They would add to and gain from the moral support which such groups exert throughout the world toward the preservation of unique natural resources and sites of historical importance. The International Union for the Conservation of Nature and Natural Resources actively seeks affiliations with governments and quasi-public agencies. Island conservation groups would be well served by joining the I.U.C.N. in its worldwide efforts to preserve the earth's natural wonders.

Planning and program personnel

Even more serious than the lack of public or quasi-public agencies is the scarcity of technically competent personnel to advise island governments or agencies in planning, facilities construction, and administration. In the area of site selection alone, many islands are without assistance. Notable exceptions are Curacao, Trinidad, Barbados, and Martinique, all fortunate in having resident scholars in the natural sciences and history who spearhead the efforts of quasi-governmental agencies in their projects for preservation and development. Less fortunate islands may be dealt with by transient scholars who appear from time to time on all the islands in the study group. However, their recommendations are typically published in journals or presented at meetings in Europe and North America. Such advice rarely reaches the eyes or ears of responsible authorities in the Caribbean, since the transient investigator often fails to contact such officials about the sites he analyzes. Thus even in this early stage of conservation programs, technical assistance is needed.

Technical assistance is needed on all the islands for the following purposes:

a. Park, reserve, and recreation area planning. Planning assistance is needed on all of the islands before they begin establishing parks and recreation areas. Since there are few technical personnel competent to do this job in the Caribbean, experienced technicians should be recruited from other parts of the world. Specifically, the islands need scientists with park and reserve experience to assist them in establishing standards for protection and development; architects and landscape architects with park and recreation area experience to assist in facilities design, park layout, and landscaping; and administrators to offer recommendations on bureaucratic structure, financing, and staffing.

b. Architectural assistance. Almost all of the islands have historic buildings of one kind or another that are in varying stages of disintegration and decay. Some islands—such as Antigua, Martinique, Guadeloupe, St. Eustatius, Curacao, and St. Kitts—have tried to stabilize or restore one or more of them. Of these islands, Antigua and St. Kitts have obtained the services of architects skilled in the restoration of historic buildings. Even on islands that might wish to utilize experienced, professional guidance for this purpose, it would be difficult to find local architects who could do the job.

c. Museum design and interpretive programs. Montserrat, Martinique, Guadeloupe, Antigua, and Trinidad have set up or are interested in setting up historical or natural history museums. On all of these islands, collections of materials are at hand, and in some cases they have been displayed. However, displays are rarely well organized or well interpreted. Assistance by qualified museum technicians could go a long way in making these valuable collections and exhibits more interesting and meaningful as well as giving them the kind of protection that is necessary.

Most interpretive programs for natural and historic areas are poorly developed. The exceptional work at Nelson's Dockyard includes a sound and light show, clearly marked and interestingly described buildings, and well written pamphlets. As in the case of museums, the creation of interpretive programs will require assistance from experienced scientists, technicians, and writers.

d. Scientific research. Studies have been made on all of the islands of the Caribbean by botanists and foresters. Rarely has research involved ecological investigation. Most botanical work dealt with collection of specimens for taxonomic study or with commercially important tree species. Studies of the fauna have followed a similar pattern and have concentrated on the identification of species and their distribution.

Much more scientific research is needed to provide a base of ecological understanding for the management of nature reserves and national park areas. Zoologists and botanists should be encouraged to study especially the ecology of unusual plant and animal communities and the life cycles of threatened endemic species. Information gained would apply directly to management programs and the development of a well-rounded interpretive program. To date, most studies of this kind have been carried out by the Foundation for Scientific Research in Surinam and the Netherlands Antilles. These, unfortunately, cover but six islands in the study group. Research grants should be made available to encourage investigation by professional biologists, ecologists, archeologists, and historians.

Educational assistance

The relationship of educational advancement to interest in conservation is a complex subject, bound up with the whole question of cultural changes. The study of Trinidad and Tobago discussed in Chapter III indicates a positive correlation between education and conservation activity of a population. One may speculate on this topic. Here a short-term approach directed at both school children and adults is suggested to accelerate public awareness of conservation goals and benefits.

It is difficult to anticipate what changes might occur in the value systems of individuals or societies if direct educational efforts were increased with regard to conservation and/or appreciation of the natural environment or the remnants of history. One such effort was a general education program begun by Bonaire in 1959 to acquaint citizens with the cultural value of the island's flamingoes and their importance to the tourism industry. Prior to this educational program, the birds were commonly taken for meat and sport, and eggs were harvested. Since the program began, there has been a steady decline of hunting and nest-robbing. In 1963 no violations of the protective laws were recorded.[3]

Conservation programs such as the creation of national parks, nature reserves, historical sites, or public recreation areas all imply a limitation of use, defined by restrictions and laws. Unless a large majority of the people respect these laws and restrictions, enforcement requires constant vigilance and physical restraint—methods which are expensive and hardly affect the roots of the problem. Whether or not we can look to public pressure as a means of giving impetus to government action in conservation, it is clear that some public awareness of the value of these sites must be achieved, as it was in the case of Bonaire's flamingoes.

If education is to be a means through which positive values relating to the natural environment and historical assets are to be created, the region will need outside help. There is a lack of both curriculum materials and qualified teachers for this type of program in the islands.

Discussions with government officials, educators, and school children on the role of science, natural history, ecology, and conservation in the curricula of the island school systems revealed the almost total lack of educational materials for such topics. There is, to the authors' knowledge, only one book on botany or zoology written specifically for school use in the Caribbean.[4] This single text itself is limited in its presentation of the ecology of the region, drawing its illustrations and examples from common cultivated and ornamental plants rather than the dynamics of natural biotic communities.

Even on the few islands where conservation and related subjects do find their way into the curriculum, students must rely entirely upon the individual instructor to present basic concepts. Not only printed materials but also teaching devices such as films, film strips, slides, and other visual aids are lacking.

Some efforts at educating the adult populations on the islands in conservation practices are carried out through the extension programs of the ministries of agriculture. However, these programs are specifically related to techniques in soil or water management as they apply directly to agriculture. The conceptual framework and principles of the subject matter are not extended to other forms of resource management.

Thus for both school age and adult populations assistance is required to create educational materials and to suggest methods and techniques for relating the materials to the present curricula of the school systems and adult programs.

XI
International Organization

The conservation of sites for national parks, nature reserves, historic monuments, and recreation areas in the Eastern Caribbean rests on activities taking place at two levels. First, concrete steps in conservation and development should take place on the individual islands, guided by the appropriate island government agencies or quasi-governmental groups such as have been discussed in earlier chapters. Second, but equally important, will be activities designed to facilitate the programs of the respective islands as carried out through a system of international co-operation among the islands and countries of the Eastern Caribbean region.

Happily, the initial organizational steps for accomplishing a program of international co-operation have already been taken. On October 1 to 4, 1965, representatives from several islands attended the Eastern Caribbean Conservation Conference at Caneel Bay, St. John, Virgin Islands. They discussed the need for conservation programs in the islands and the organizational requirements for accomplishing conservation throughout the region. The conference resolved to establish an international body called the Caribbean Conservation Association. The Association was formed in May, 1967, by delegates from the U. S. Virgin Islands, Jamaica,

Barbados, Grenada, St. Lucia, St. Kitts, Trinidad and Tobago, and Venezuela.

The intentions of this new organization are modest and worthwhile. The Association assumes no prerogatives for direct action on the islands. Rather, it seeks to become a forum for discussion of conservation issues, a co-ordinator of outside technical and financial assistance, and a persuasive influence for action on the part of individual islands, their governments, and their related conservation groups. In these respects, the Caribbean Conservation Association embodies the idea that there is a Caribbean regional context which needs expression in the field of conservation as well as in the more commonly recognized social, economic, and political areas.

This idea, we believe, is well tuned to the current problems of the Eastern Caribbean. It is consistent with the recommendation of the *Economic Survey of the Eastern Caribbean* that the regional nature of the islands should be emphasized in the development of tourism. The Caribbean Conservation Association substantiates the belief that there are resources important to the region that should receive high priority for conservation efforts of the several participating islands and countries. In this respect, the Association can do for regional resources what the individual island agencies or trusts can do for their own resources.

The critical issue for the future of the Caribbean Conservation Association lies not with its intentions or its potentials. It lies with its ability to execute those intentions through an on-going program. The new Association is faced with the same fundamental problems which confront the individual island agencies—the difficulty of financing programs and securing the necessary technical competence.

The eventual success of this group depends on the degree to which it can elicit interest and support from sources of aid outside the region, and the degree to which such sources recognize the Caribbean Conservation Association as a logical channel through which to respond. The practical advantages to be gained, it seems to us, are obvious. First, there are resources which have regional value for which a regional group logically ought to be spokesman. Second, as a co-ordinating agency it can better direct the efforts of specialized professionals whose services are needed throughout the Caribbean region. Third, it is in a position to retain the historic and scientific integrity of the natural and historic resources because that is its primary interest, even though its efforts may be realistically related to the goals of developing tourism.

Cast in this last role particularly, the Association is capable of filling a position that is unlikely to be filled by any other type of institution. Acting as a corollary to an individual island trust or society, the Association can help ensure that the cultural character of the resources is conserved on the highest plane for the benefit of the region's population as well as visitors.

The Caribbean Conservation Association represents the first step toward regional conservation. Its objectives are impeccable, but it has no material power to affect decision-making on any individual island. We hope that the Association will develop into an institution with greater organizational integrity and more effective influence on the course of conservation efforts in the region. Ideally, we believe this might take the form of a Caribbean international park system.

What is needed in the Caribbean is an idea appealing enough to sustain the already expressed interests of the few people and governments in the Caribbean who are concerned about nature and history, and an idea big enough to incite action by political decision-makers who have, up to this point, not been involved in the conservation of natural, scenic, and historical areas.

A Caribbean international park system might fill this role. First, it would allow for co-ordinated development programs of resources within a natural bio-physical region, and one with an integrated history. Second, it could provide the psychological lift to overcome the inertia that has built up through generations of inactivity in conservation of nature, historical sites, and outdoor recreation areas.

The concept of internationalizing certain aspects of parks or historical sites in the Caribbean is not new. Thought has already been given to a Virgin Islands international park,[1] and to an international program of historical site development to commemorate the voyages and discoveries of Columbus.[2] Although nothing material has resulted from these suggestions, they may be valued as attempts to create a universe of understanding and operation in a disjunct cultural and political region.

The problems in establishing a Virgin Islands international park were due in significant part to an emotionally charged atmosphere in St. John, United States Virgin Islands. The people there feared that the United States National Park Service would apply an unreasoned and heavy hand in condemnation of private lands within the boundaries of the park. These fears were transferred to the people of the neighboring British Virgin Islands so that public opinion was against the establishment of an international park boundary encompassing both United States and British islands.[3]

The proposal to develop a system of historic sites commemorating Columbus' voyages is undermined by the paucity of physical evidence of his presence. He actually had little to do with the islands beyond discovering them and in many cases naming them.

Perhaps a Virgin Islands international park and a series of commemorative historical sites are concepts too small or too vague. Neither idea adequately captured the imaginations of local people or political leaders.

The concept of a Caribbean international park system containing natural areas, historical sites, and other recreation areas presents an undertaking of sufficient scope to capture the imaginations of the people on the islands. So many different islands and resources would be involved that a few sites could be incorporated into the system in rather short order. Operating on the theory that nothing succeeds like success, there is every hope that examples set by completed projects on one island would help to erase apathy or misgivings that may exist on another island. Even though some projects might be delayed or even fail altogether, there would still be a body of successful experience from which to learn and take encouragement.

Beyond providing a stronger psychological climate, does the idea of a Caribbean international park system relate to the economic problems of the region? If it takes a bigger idea to impel action within the region itself, it may also take a bigger idea to entice potential tourists to the area.

The basic resources for an international system are certainly present. However, longstanding competition and social-economic isolation have repeatedly thwarted attempts to effectively co-operate in solving mutual problems. Despite the undercurrent of popular feeling that the islands must form more effective social, political, and economic ties, success in doing so is rare. The Caribbean Organization, now defunct, marked a recent effort by the islands and countries of the Caribbean to work together in the fields of agriculture, economic development, and cultural affairs. In matters of research, education, cultural exchange, and development of tourism, the Organization had support from all members. However, programs to develop trade unions, remove tariffs, and increase the freedom of intra-regional migration have consistently failed.[4]

Reality, then, sets limits on the nature of any proposals for internationalizing the development of natural and historic resources. The options for real action in the field of conservation remain with the respective governments of the islands. We believe that any suggestions to transfer those options to an international body will be met with strong negative response.

An international system for developing parks and equivalent reserves should be limited to providing the kinds of services and encouragement that allow island governments and leaders to exercise their options wisely. Participation in it should offer benefits attractive enough to enlist the co-operation of island governments.

The park system should restrict its operations to activities that island governments are willing to accept. The system should treat with the basic problems outlined in the preceding chapter—especially those of professional skills, educational programs, and relating the natural and historic resources to tourism. To the extent that the co-operative system exercises control, it should be limited to mutually agreed-upon minimum standards for development of the several classes of sites. Thus, any site on a co-operating island, developed to meet those standards, could be included in the international park system.

This approach to international co-operation in park management has worked effectively since 1932 at the Waterton-Glacier International Peace Park on the border between the United States and Canada. Between Poland and Czechoslovakia, one border park was created in 1932, and another in the years 1948-1954. In none of these parks is there joint dominion of the park land. Co-ordination of park management is secured by international agreements covering facilities development, forest management, wildlife protection, and other aspects. Co-operation also extends to scientific study and tourism development.[5]

The Latin American Committee on National Parks co-ordinates the development of administrative standards for national parks and reserves in many of the nations of South and Central America. The intention in this case is not to create an international park system, but rather to create a common understanding of how and why individual countries should develop their own internal park systems.

Our suggestions for a Caribbean international park system embody both the idea of international agreement on common standards and the idea of an international agency to co-ordinate park development in the region's islands and countries.

Administration of the Caribbean international park system

The park system should be governed by a committee made up of representatives from each of the responsible agencies, both government and quasi-government, from the islands participating in the system. Responsibilities of the committee should include the following:

1. The committee should carry on a continuing effort to acquire funds for the operation of the park system.

2. The committee should establish standards for protection and levels of development for all classes of natural, historical, and recreation areas within the system. The committee should function as advisor to the several governments on legislation for the establishment and protection of the several classes of sites.

3. The committee should establish priority ratings for developing resources within the park system with respect to the relative importance of these resources from scientific, historical, cultural, and economic points of view.

4. The committee should make recommendations to the several governments in the region on educational programs designed to promote public appreciation and awareness of the cultural and economic value of the sites.

5. The committee should create a body of materials on the international park system applicable to the promotional campaigns of the Caribbean Tourist Association, the respective island tourist boards, travel agencies, steamship lines, and airlines.

6. The committee should appoint an advisory board made up of scholars in science, history, and archeology to assist the committee in all phases of its deliberations pertaining to site selection, development priority, educational policies, and legislation.

7. The committee should maintain an office to carry out the recommended projects.

The executive director

The directives of the governing committee should be carried out by an executive director. The executive director should be a person competent in the technical and administrative aspects of park and recreation systems. He should be capable of advising the governing committee and the island agencies on technical aspects of establishing, developing, and administering national parks, reserves, historical sites, and public outdoor recreation areas. The executive director should be provided with an office and staff to perform tasks assigned by the governing committee. The day-to-day function of the executive director's office might include the following:

1. The office could serve as a source of direct technical aid to the island agencies in the development of national parks, historical sites, and recreation areas.

2. The office could serve visiting scientists, historians, and archeologists doing work in the Caribbean. In this capacity, the executive director would keep in close contact with universities and other research institutions that might be sending research personnel to the region. The office could supply researchers with letters of introduction, background orientation, and liaison between experts with common or parallel interests.

3. The office could assist in creating and editing materials for classroom use and outlines for incorporating conservation studies into the existing curricula of the school systems. In addition, the office could organize workshops for teachers and school administrators to acquaint them with the techniques for teaching conservation at various grade levels and demonstrating the usefulness of parks and other sites as outdoor laboratories and educational tools.

4. The office could prepare material on the park system for mass media presentation within the region.

5. The office could develop a newsletter containing feature articles on various parks and historical sites in the system as well as details of specific regional conservation problems. The purpose of the newsletter would be to inform interested persons and agencies about the progress and problems of the international park system.

6. The office could work closely with the island tourist boards and with travel agencies, airlines, and steamship companies to assist in promoting the Caribbean international park system as an attraction for tourists.

Financing

Ideally, the cost of maintaining the office of the executive director should be shared by all of the islands participating in the international park system. However, the lack of financial resources among the islands and their respective agencies is not likely to be overcome in the near future. While the islands perhaps could afford to pay part of the costs, we believe that the major financial burden would have to be borne by interested persons or governments outside the Caribbean region. Hopefully, economic conditions on the Caribbean islands will improve in the future to the point where public and private sources of money will be available for nature preservation and historical site development. The islands could then maintain complete financial responsibility for the operation of the entire Caribbean international park system.

Conclusion

A regional conservation program in the Caribbean is urgently needed. Little remains of the unique natural features and records of aboriginal and early European settlement, and what does remain is vulnerable to destruction in the name of economic advancement. Our plea is not to arrest the economic progress of men in order to conserve nature and history, but to pursue both goals in concert. This could be accomplished by the islands with assistance from the continental nations that have shared in the history of the Caribbean. The international context for conservation which we propose is consistent with the prevailing undercurrent of island political thought, and it offers the means for making the most effective use of money and expertise available to the region.

Notes

Chapter II

1. Caribbean Organization, *Caribbean Plan Annual Report, 1962* (Hato Rey, Puerto Rico: Central Secretariat, Caribbean Organization, 1963), pp. 1-2.

2. Charles Schuchert, *Historical Geology of the Antillean-Caribbean Region* (New York: John Wiley & Sons, Inc., 1935), pp. 9-29, 391-540; and Ralph A. Liddle, *The Geology of Venezuela and Trinidad* (Ithaca, New York: Paleontological Research Institution, 1946), pp. 683-793.

3. Information summarized in this section was drawn from: J. A. Bullbrook, *The Aborigines of Trinidad* (Port of Spain, Trinidad: Royal Victoria Institute Museum, 1960); Société d'Histoire de la Martinique, *First International Convention for the Study of Pre-Columbian Culture in the Lesser Antilles, Part I* (Fort-de-France, Martinique: Société d'Histoire de la Martinique, 1963); C. Jesse, *The Amerindians in St. Lucia* (Castries, St. Lucia: St. Lucia Archeological Historical Society, 1960); and J. H. Parry and P. M. Sherlock, *A Short History of the West Indies* (London: Macmillan & Co. Ltd., 1960).

4. Société d'Histoire de la Martinique, *op. cit.,* p. 94.

5. The following books on Caribbean history, from which the material for this section was drawn, are recommended as sources of detailed information: Alan Cuthbert Burns, *History of the British West Indies* (London: George Allen & Unwin

Ltd., 1954); Richard Pares, *War and Trade in the West Indies* (Oxford: Clarenden Press, 1936); and Parry and Sherlock, *op. cit.*

Chapter III

1. Information for this topic was drawn from: *The West Indies and Caribbean Yearbook: 1963* (London: Thomas Skinner & Co., Ltd., 1962); conversations with government officials of the islands studied; and *The New York Times,* November 30, 1966, p. 20.

2. E. Gordon Erickson, *The West Indies Population Problem* (Lawrence, Kansas: The University of Kansas Publications, 1962), p. 115.

3. Caribbean Organization, *Caribbean Plan Annual Report, 1963* (Hato Rey, Puerto Rico: Central Secretariat, Caribbean Organization, 1964), p. 2.

4. Erickson, *op. cit.,* pp. 114-15.

5. Caribbean Organization, . . . *Report, 1963;* and . . . *Report, 1962.*

6. *Report of the Tripartite Economic Survey of the Eastern Caribbean* (To the Governments of the United Kingdom of Great Britain and Northern Ireland, of Canada and of the United States of America, 1966), Preface.

7. Caribbean Organization, . . . *Report, 1963,* p. 72.

8. *Tripartite Economic Survey,* II. 2,3.

9. W. Arthur Lewis, "Social Services in Development Planning," *Planning for Economic Development in the Caribbean,* ed. Caribbean Organization (Hato Rey, Puerto Rico: Central Secretariat, Caribbean Organization, 1963), pp. 158-59.

10. Tripartite Economic Survey, II.7.6.

11. Monte Hilliard Koppel and Carl A. Carlozzi, "Leisure Time in Trinidad: Activities, Meaning and Significance" (Report for the American Conservation Association, Inc., New York, 1963), pp. 35-36. (Multilithed.)

12. Caribbean Organization, . . . *Report, 1963,* pp. 71,139.

13. *Ibid.,* p. 139; and Caribbean Organization, . . . *Report, 1962,* p. 254.

14. Caribbean Organization, . . . *Report, 1963,* p. 139.

15. Information on Tobago was obtained through interviews with Joe Crooks, Chief Town and Country Planner, and Brigid Massiah, Five Year Planning Office, of the Trinidad and Tobago government in October, 1963.

16. Caribbean Organization, . . . *Report, 1963,* pp. 138, 143.

17. *Ibid.,* p. 71.

18. *Ibid.,* p. 139.

19. Erickson, *op. cit.,* p. 33.

20. *Tripartite Economic Survey,* Table 16.

21. Interview with John C. Phillips, Director of Agriculture, Montserrat, November 23, 1963.

22. Caribbean Organization, . . . *Report, 1963,* p. 11.

23. *Ibid.,* p. 139; and interview with Herve Bizien, SITO Delegate, Martinique, March 10, 1964.

24. Derived from Table 8, *Tripartite Economic Survey.*

25. Caribbean Organization, . . . *Report, 1963,* pp. 124, 139.

26. *Tripartite Economic Survey,* II.2.90.

27. Caribbean Organization, . . . *Report, 1963,* p. 139.

Chapter IV

1. P. W. Richards, *The Tropical Rain Forest: An Ecological Study* (Cambridge: Cambridge University Press, 1964), p. 2.

2. Jane's (1930) translation, quoted in Richards, *op. cit.,* p. 1.

3. J. S. Beard, *The Natural Vegetation of the Windward & Leeward Islands* ("Oxford Forestry Memoirs," No. 21, 1948; London: Oxford University Press, 1949); p. 50. This classification system is presently recognized as the standard treatment of vegetation types throughout the Caribbean. It is used almost verbatim by A. L. Stoffers in *The Vegetation of the Netherlands Antilles* ("Studies on the Flora of Curacao and Other Caribbean Islands,"

Vol. I; The Hague: Martinus Nijhoff, 1956); and it is recommended by Stanley A. Cain and G. M. de Olivera Castro in their *Manual of Vegetation Analysis* (New York: Harper Bros., 1959), p. 50.

4. Beard, *op. cit.*, pp. 11-49.

5. Richard A. Howard, "Suggestions for the Preservation of Botanical Species Endemic to the Islands of the Antilles." Paper presented at the Third General Assembly, International Union for the Protection of Nature, Caracas, Venezuela, September, 1952. (Mimeographed.)

6. Beard, *op. cit.*, p. 50.

7. Howard, *op. cit.*

8. J. H. Westermann, *Conservation in the Caribbean* ("Publications of the Foundation for Scientific Research in Surinam and the Netherlands Antilles," No. 7; The Hague: Martinus Nijhoff, 1952), p. 47.

9. J. H. Westermann, *Nature Preservation in the Caribbean* ("Publications of the Foundation for Scientific Research in Surinam and the Netherlands Antilles," No. 9; Utrecht, Holland: The Foundation . . ., 1953).

10. *Ibid.*

11. *Ibid.*, chapters 2, 3, and 4; and James Bond, *Birds of the West Indies* (Boston: Houghton Mifflin Co., 1961).

12. Westermann, *Nature Preservation* . . ., p. 15.

13. Interview with Hollis Murray, Conservator of Forests, Trinidad and Tobago, May 2, 1964.

14. Westermann, *Nature Preservation* . . ., p. 14.

15. Information for this topic was drawn from Westermann, *Nature Preservation* . . ., chapter 6; and conversations with island government officials.

Chapter V

1. Association for Tropical Biology, *Proceedings of the Neotropical Botany Conference*, Bulletin No. 1 (Trinidad, W.I.: Tri Color Printery Ltd., for U.W.I.—I.C.T.A.), p. 72.

2. *Ibid.,* p. 74.

3. Beard, *op. cit.,* p. 50.

Chapter VI

1. Westermann, *Nature Preservation . . .,* p. 15.

2. R. Pinchon, *Faune des Antilles Francaises: Les Oiseaux* (Fort de France, Martinique: 1963).

3. Interview with R. Pinchon, March 11, 1964.

4. Interview with Jacques Petitjean-Roget, President, Martinique History Society, March 9, 1964.

5. Interview with Kingsley Howes, November 19, 1963.

6. Westermann, *Conservation in the Caribbean;* and Stoffers, *op. cit.*

7. Stoffers, *op. cit.,* pp. 101-102.

8. G. H. King, "Brimstone Hill: The Gibraltar of the West Indies," 1965 edition, Reprinted by the National Geographic Society.

9. Beard, *op. cit.,* p. 143.

10. Interview with Hollis Murray, Conservator of Forests, Trinidad and Tobago Forest Department, October 24, 1963.

11. Interview with Hollis Murray, October 24, 1963.

12. Interview with Michael Bayne, Acting Conservator of Forests, Trinidad and Tobago, November 9, 1962.

13. Interview with John W. Purseglove, University of the West Indies, November 7, 1962.

Chapter VII

1. Interview with Fred Olsen, President of the Antigua Archaeological Society, Ltd., March, 1963.

2. Interview with A. W. Symmonds, Permanent Secretary, Ministry of Home Affairs, Barbados, April, 1967.

3. Beard, *op. cit.,* p. 94.

4. *Ibid.,* p. 86.

Chapter VIII

1. Interview with Ingvar Kristensen, Secretary, Netherlands Antilles National Parks Foundation, November 20, 1962.

2. Letter from Ingvar Kristensen, April 17, 1964.

Chapter IX

1. *Tripartite Economic Survey,* II.3.

2. *Ibid.,* II.3.25.

3. *Ibid.,* II.3.

4. *Ibid.*

5. Caribbean Organization, . . . *Report, 1963,* pp. 10-11.

6. *Ibid.,* p. 10.

7. *Ibid.*

8. *Clearing House on Trade and Tourism Information,* II, No. 6 (Puerto Rico: Caribbean Organization, June, 1963), p. 29.

9. Anglo-American Caribbean Commission, *Caribbean Tourist Trade: a Regional Approach* (Washington: 1945), p. 7.

10. Caribbean Organization, *Planning for Economic Development in the Caribbean* (Hato Rey, Puerto Rico: Central Secretariat, Caribbean Organization, 1963), p. 94.

11. Carl A. Carlozzi, "Economic Development on St. John, Virgin Islands: 1955-1963." Report for the American Conservation Association, Inc., New York, 1963. (Multilithed.)

12. Floyd K. Harmston, Richard E. Lund, and J. Richard Williams, *A Study of the Resources, People, and Economy of Teton County, Wyoming* (Cheyenne, Wyoming: Wyoming Natural Resource Board, 1959), pp. 36-7.

13. Carl A. Carlozzi, "A Report on the Development of Parks, Nature Reserves and Outdoor Recreation Areas in Trinidad and Tobago." (Report for the Town and Country Planning Division, Office of the Prime Minister, Trinidad and Tobago: 1964, Mimeographed).

Chapter X

1. Caribbean Organization, . . . *Report, 1963,* pp. 141-143.

2. Interview with R. Pinchon, March 11, 1964.

3. Interview with A. J. van Hesteren, Lieutenant Governor of Bonaire, November 17, 1963.

4. E. T. Robertson and E. G. B. Gooding, *Botany for the Caribbean* (London: Collins Clear-Type Press, 1963).

Chapter XI

1. Interview with John Lewis, Superintendent, Virgin Islands National Park, December 4, 1962.

2. Interview with Conrad Wirth, Director, U. S. National Park Service, July 3, 1962.

3. Interview with John Lewis, December 4, 1962.

4. Interview with Hugh Miller, Agricultural Secretary, Caribbean Organization, May 7, 1964.

5. Walery Goetel, "Parks Between Countries," *First World Conference on National Parks* (Washington: National Park Service, U. S. Department of Interior, 1962), pp. 287-294.

Index